Macmillan Building and Surveying Guide

Series Editor: Ivor H. Seeley

Emeritus Professor, Nottingham Trent University

Series Standing Order

If you would like to receive future titles in this series as they are
published, you can make use of our standing order facility. To place
a standing order please contact your bookseller or, in case of difficulty,
write to us at the address below with your name and address and the
name of the series. Please state with which title you wish to begin your
standing order. (If you live outside the United Kingdom we may not
have the rights for your area, in which case we will forward your order
to the publisher concerned.)

Customer Services Department, Macmillan Distribution Ltd
Houndmills, Basingstoke, Hampshire, RG21 2XS, England.

Introduction to Building Services

Second Edition

E.F. Curd and C.A. Howard
School of the Built Environment
Liverpool John Moores University

MACMILLAN

First edition 1988
Second edition 1996

Published by
MACMILLAN PRESS LTD
Houndmills, Basingstoke, Hampshire RG21 6XS
and London
Companies and representatives
throughout the world

ISBN 0–333–59911–X

A catalogue record for this book is available
from the British Library.

10   9   8   7   6   5   4   3   2   1
05   04   03   02   01   00   99   98   97   96

Printed in Hong Kong

CONTENTS

Appendices

PREFACE

This book is intended as a textbook for use by students of quantity surveying, building surveying, estate management, architecture and building up to degree level. It can also be used as an introduction for students of building services engineering.

Some students find the important topic of building services difficult to grasp. This is because they are unable to associate it with their future profession, or relate it to the environmental science topics covered in the course of their study.

The method of treatment in this book is to provide individual students or whole classes with a teaching approach of sufficient clarity that the student, presumably unfamiliar with the topic, will not be confused, and to give sufficient coverage of the topics to provide solid theoretical groundwork together with some knowledge of practice.

This second edition has been prepared in order to bring the book up to date with recent developments in the field since the first edition was written.

All chapters have been revised, and new chapters added, together with an appendix covering some of the basic equations used in building services engineering. An important new feature, which the authors believe will find favour with both lecturers and students, is the model questions given at the end of each chapter.

As British, European and international standards, as well as the UK Building Regulations, have changed considerably since the first edition, this new edition allows these to be brought up to date. It must be remembered, however, that all BS and CEN (European) standards are in a state of flux, and reference should always be made to the current standards. It is recommended that *Environmental Science in Buildings* by Randall McMullan (Macmillan, 3rd edn, 1992) is read in conjunction with this book in order to clarify and augment the relationship between environmental science and building services.

E.F. Curd
C.A. Howard
1996

1 COLD WATER INSTALLATIONS: SUPPLY AND DISTRIBUTION

INTRODUCTION

In building services applications, water is used in many ways.

Briefly, these are as follows:

- cold water for drinking;
- cold water supplied to a domestic hot water cylinder or boiler for domestic washing or industrial process purposes;
- cold water supplied to refrigeration plant for chilling (this chilled water is then distributed to the air conditioning system or cooling plant);
- cold water for sanitary appliances;
- cold water for filling the heating system;
- cold water for fire-fighting services.

The cold water may be obtained directly from the water mains or from a tank. In the UK the mains water can be assumed to have a seasonal average temperature of 10°C.

The quality and the nature of water entering a building will vary. However, it is essential to ensure certain standards of purity for each of the above applications. The EC Directive 80/778 deals with the quality of water for human consumption.

WATER SUPPLY

In Britain about 10 per cent of the rainfall finds its way into the distribution mains; the remainder is either absorbed into the ground, evaporates, or runs off into rivers or streams. Rainfall flows from upland sources to the regional reservoirs, where some sedimentation of the larger particulate matter takes place.

The water from a reservoir is treated to remove the suspended organic and inorganic materials. This process is necessary to destroy pathogenic bacteria, which can cause typhoid, cholera or other disease. The process consists of:

(1) coarse straining of the water to remove large floating objects;
(2) sedimentation to remove small, high-density impurities;
(3) filtration through sand beds to remove the smaller suspended solids and attached bacteria;
(4) sterilization by injection with chlorine or treatment with ozone before pumping into the mains.

In the UK it is a statutory requirement of the Water Acts that every dwelling is supplied with water fit for drinking. A typical arrangement of the above sequence is shown in Figure 1.1. The mains are arranged in a ring to ensure that during mains repairs only a part of the circuit is isolated.

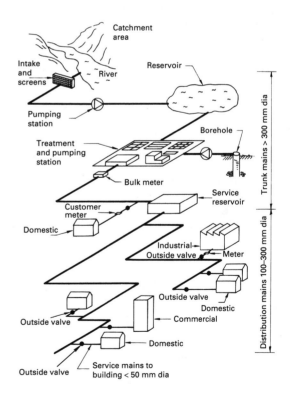

Figure 1.1 Mains water supply

NATURE OF WATER

Pure water is tasteless, colourless and odourless, and is a simple combination of hydrogen and oxygen (H_2O). Within the natural temperature range of the earth, water can exist in three forms: ice, water and steam.

Water occurs in several hybrid forms. One is deuterium (D_2O): this is known as heavy water, as used in nuclear reactors. About 300 parts per million is in this form. Another form of water is tritium oxide (T_2O), although only a very small amount is in this form. It is produced by radioactivity from cosmic rays and its magnitude can be used for measuring the age of a water supply. In this study only simple water (H_2O) will be considered.

Pure water cannot be found outside the laboratory, because all natural waters contain many impurities to different levels.

These impurities can be classed as:

● dissolved solids;
● dissolved gases;
● suspended solids.

Water is a solvent, and thus when in contact with soil or rock, it dissolves the solids in the ground. Gases in the air and organic matter in the soil are also dissolved in the water.

Further contamination occurs from suspended matter in the earth, as well as from wastes from agricultural and industrial processes, the magnitude depending on the contact time.

Water that flows though the strata of rocks dissolves and absorbs the various minerals of which the rock is composed. These minerals include calcium carbonate (limestone), calcium sulphate (gypsum), magnesium sulphate (Epsom salts), silica (sand), sodium chloride (common salt) and hydrated sodium sulphate (Glauber salts), as well as iron, manganese, flouride, aluminium and dissolved gases.

Water is classified as either **hard** or **soft**. Hard water contains the mineral salts of calcium or magnesium carbonate and bicarbonate. With this type of water, it is difficult to produce a lather with soap.

The amount of hardness may vary with the amount of mineral salts, which can vary from a few parts per million (ppm) to over 300 ppm. Table 1.1 shows six classifications of water according to hardness.

Calcium and magnesium carbonates and bicar-

Table 1.1 *Water classification*

Designation	Parts per million (ppm or mg/l)
Soft	0– 50
Moderately soft	50–100
Slightly hard	100–150
Moderately hard	150–200
Hard	200–300
Very hard	over 300

bonates are relatively insoluble in water, and as the solubility of these salts decreases with an increase of temperature, they tend to be precipitated out on surrounding surfaces. These liberated salts cause a scale build-up on the waterside of heat transfer equipment, resulting in a serious reduction in thermal efficiency and in the water flow rate.

The hardness caused by these salts is known as **temporary** hardness, and can be removed completely from solution by boiling. The type of hardness known as **permanent** is caused by the presence of non-carbonate salts, such as calcium sulphate, calcium chloride and magnesium chloride, as well as other sulphates and chlorides. These salts cannot be removed by boiling; they can only be removed by the technical use of chemical reactions.

Water passing over and through peaty ground picks up humic acid, causing it to become acidic and soft. Water of this type requires less soap than hard water to produce a lather. It is corrosive to steel, and if it is used in lead pipe the solvent reaction removes the lead from the pipe (the water is said to be **plumbo-solvent**). Lead in drinking water is dangerous to health and hence lead pipes are no longer permitted in new buildings. Under certain conditions soft water removes the zinc from gunmetal pipe fittings, causing them to break down, a phenomenon known as **dezincification.** The best pipes to use in soft water areas are copper or plastic.

The **pH scale** is used to denote the degree of acidity or alkalinity of the water. An acid water has a pH of less than 7.0, while an alkaline water has a pH greater than 7.0. The range of pH depends on the nature of the ground over which the water flows. Typical values for the pH of natural waters range from 6.0 for moorland waters to 8.0 for waters containing carbonate hardness and little free dissolved carbon dioxide.

The water used in boiler and air-conditioning plant requires chemical treatment in order to ensure that scale formation does not affect the plant's performance. Any air in the system has to be removed in order to reduce metal corrosion due to free oxygen.

Domestic hot water and cooling towers require chemical treatment in order to reduce or eliminate the bacterium *legionella pneumophilia* which causes legionnaires' disease.

Many methods of water treatment are used for removing the hardness salts. It is sufficient at this stage to briefly consider a few of these. If all the mineral salts have to be removed, as is required in certain manufacturing processes or in power station boilers, the raw water passes through certain ion exchange resins. This process is known as **demineralization.**

The method most commonly used is the **base-exchange** process. In this process the raw mains water passes into a filter tank containing sodium zeolite, where a base exchange occurs. The calcium and the sodium are exchanged, so that the water that leaves the tank contains sodium carbonate (which in most cases presents no problems), while the sodium zeolite in the tank is gradually converted to calcium zeolite. Eventually the filter bed becomes saturated, and the efficiency of the process reduces to zero. By back-washing the filter bed with a brine solution (sodium chloride) a reverse exchange is made to occur, restoring the calcium zeolite to sodium zeolite, and allowing the process to operate at maximum efficiency once more.

SUPPLIES TO LOW-RISE BUILDINGS

Domestic low-rise dwellings of single-, two- or three-storey construction are connected to the water main by a service branch pipe, as shown in Figure 1.2.

The main features of this arrangement are as follows.

- The water authority or others can disconnect the supply by means of the stopcock located outside the house boundary.
- The pipe is usually laid at a depth not less than 1 m, which in the UK will prevent freezing during the winter months.

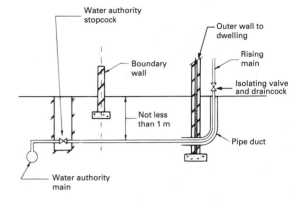

Figure 1.2 Cold water supply: typical domestic service pipe

- A duct is provided to carry the supply into the building through the wall and floor.
- On entering the building near floor level the rising main has an isolating valve with a draincock to allow drainage of the pipe above this point.

In older property lead service pipes may still be found. However, the Model Water Byelaw 9 [1] prohibits the use of lead in new buildings. This includes lead pipes and water fittings, as well as storage cisterns made from, or internally lined with, lead, and applies both to new installations and the repair or replacement of existing lead pipes and cisterns. The purpose of this regulation is to remove the risk of lead poisoning.

All modern installations are provided with blue polyethylene pipe to BS 6572 [2] for below-ground use with cold potable water, or other approved materials. Black polyethylene pipe to BS 6730 [3] may be used for cold water services above ground.

The increasing use of plastics pipes has presented problems of **electrical earthing**. An earth wire, clamped to a metal pipe buried in the ground, allows an earth path. However, if this metal pipe is replaced by a plastic pipe, the earth path is destroyed. Hence care has to be taken with modifications to cold water systems, to ensure that a separate earthing system is provided. This is an important point to check on every building survey; any failure to ensure an adequate earth, which causes the electrocution of a person, will lead to acrimonious litigation.

Once the service pipe emerges from the floor it is called the **rising main**; it is required to have a stopcock and drain point provided at the lowest point. The distance of this rising main from the wall must meet the requirement of Byelaw 49 [1].

Figure 1.3 shows a typical cold water installation for a domestic two-storey building [4]. Note that the rising main, on entering the building is piped to a ball valve, which feeds the water into the high-level storage tank. In this **direct** system the sanitary appliances are connected directly to the rising main. The older **indirect** system provides a gravity supply of cold water to the sanitary appliances from the cold water storage tank and not directly from the rising main.

The minimum mains pressure in the street is 100 kPa; this pressure will allow water to rise 10 m, which is adequate for most domestic buildings. Mains pressures higher than this are available, the pressure depending on the location of the take-off to the pumping station or the elevation of the external storage reservoir.

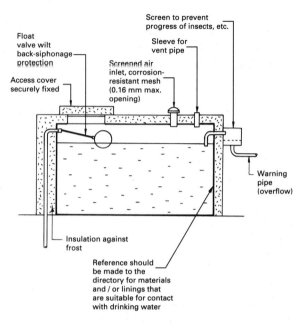

Figure 1.4   Storage cistern, showing some of the requirements of Water Byelaw 30. The directory referred to is the regulatory standard that covers water fittings

It is essential to ensure that contamination of the stored water does not take place, and all storage tanks must meet the requirements of Byelaw 30 [1]. This regulation is designed to ensure that no contaminant can pass through the overflow or lid of the storage tank. Figure 1.4 illustrates the requirements of some parts of this regulation. The Water Regulations are designed to ensure that **back-siphonage** will not occur. If a pressure reduction takes place on a tap in the incoming cold main, and this tap has a hose connected to some contaminated water, the resulting suction effect (back-siphonage) will allow contaminated water to enter the drinking water main.

A mains-pressure branch may also be taken from the rising main to the WC. If this is the case, it must have a double check valve assembly and a high-pressure ball valve. The check valve arrangement will only allow water to flow from the main to the appliance, and not in reverse.

The flushing system in new installations will have a dual flush, providing a single flush not exceed-

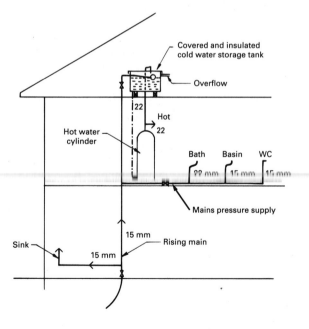

Figure 1.3   Typical two-storey domestic cold water installation

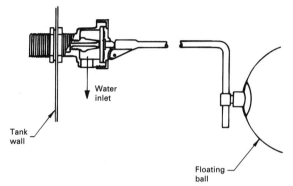

Figure 1.5 Typical ball valve assembly

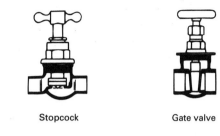

Figure 1.6 Typical valves

ing 7.5 litres, or a double flush of 9.5 litres. The reason for this is to economize on water usage. Figure 1.5 shows a typical ball valve assembly (see [5]), although a number of different valve types are available. In the past the ball float was constructed from copper; however, plastics floats have now replaced copper for domestic installations. Various types of float are available, but all those used in the UK must meet the requirements of the Water Byelaws.

In indirect systems the water from the cold water storage cistern (tank) is supplied to the domestic hot water cylinder and the bathroom sanitary appliances. The down feed from the cistern is at tank head pressure, and not at mains pressure.

It is essential to have adequate isolating valves on a system so that the water supply can be closed down (see Figure 1.3) without the need to drain the whole system. This is required in order to change tap washers, to repair leaks or to allow ball valve servicing.

In services work many types of valve are used; two important examples are the **stopcock** and the **gate valve.** Figure 1.6 shows the difference between these: the stopcock body is a different shape from the gate valve, and the stopcock has a straight bar head, whereas the gate valve has a wheel head.

Cold water storage cisterns are either manufactured from plastics or galvanised mild steel. Very large ones are made from cast iron. They are often located in the roof space and must be protected against freezing. The Building Regulations require the roof space to be ventilated in order to prevent condensation [6]. The Water Byelaws also require

the tank to be thermally insulated. The storage tank reduces the sudden demand for water and also provides ample storage capacity [7], which should cope with short-term interruption of the mains supply.

A typical domestic cistern will store 230 litres. Cisterns can also be located in cupboards, usually above the domestic hot water cylinder; alternatively these may be provided as a complete prefabricated set.

Copper pipe to BS 2871 (Tables X, Y and Z) [8] is used in buildings. Unlike steel pipe, which is sized on its internal bore, copper pipe is classed according to its external diameter, following ISO convention. The standard diameters (in mm) are 15, 22, 28, 35, 42 and 54.

Discolouration of the water supply will not occur owing to rusting, as can happen with steel pipes. Small-diameter copper pipes are joined with capillary fittings (soldered) or compression fittings (nutted) as shown in Figure 1.7. The latter are more expensive, but have the advantage of being easy to dismantle. Care has to be taken with soldered joints, as the flux used on the solder is corrosive, and can cause the breakdown of mild steel radiators in the system.

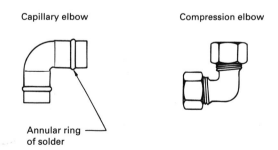

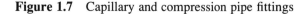

Figure 1.7 Capillary and compression pipe fittings

Other pipe materials used for cold water systems are unplasticized PVC (PVC-U) or polyethylene, up to a nominal size of 63 mm. Different jointing techniques are used for these, depending on the size.

The choice of material must comply with the Byelaws, and the designer will select a suitable material, bearing in mind the following factors:

- *Copper*. Easier to joint than steel or cast iron; it is used for hot or cold water and gas supply.
- *Stainless steel*. Provides good standards of hygiene, making it suitable for food processing and hospitals; it has the disadvantage of being the most expensive pipework.
- *ABS* (acrilonitrile-butadiene-styrene): this material has a high impact strength and is non-toxic, making it suitable for the chemical and pharmaceutical industries, as well as for limited use in domestic installations.
- *PVC-U*. At low temperatures its impact strength deteriorates: hence care has to be taken in its application.

As plastics pipes have a high rate of thermal expansion, care has to be taken in using them when hot water is conveyed, to ensure that thermal expansion does not pull the joints out. The operating pressure limits of these materials are not as high as those of steel or copper.

When making changes in pipework size or direction, either purpose-made fittings or bends are employed. Figure 1.8 shows the use of a bending spring for thin-wall pipes. For heavier-wall pipes, a bending machine is used. A machine of this type is also used for bending electrical conduit. Purpose-made fittings are also used to make junctions between pipes, or to connect pipes to appliances.

SUPPLIES TO HIGH-RISE BUILDINGS

Regardless of the building type (low rise or high rise), the object of the water supply system is to ensure a continuous and adequate supply of water to the building. In the early part of the 20th century, the high-level reservoir was capable of providing this rate of supply, and adequate pressure

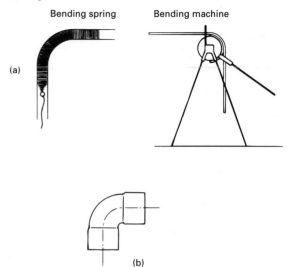

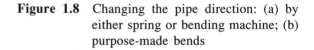

Figure 1.8 Changing the pipe direction: (a) by either spring or bending machine; (b) purpose-made bends

head to low-rise buildings. However, with the need for high-rise buildings, this traditional method is no longer feasible.

It would not be practical for the water authority to increase the mains pressure to serve all high-rise buildings, as this would lead to bursts in older mains and fittings. The only way to overcome the problem of pressure head is to boost the pressure at the entry into the building. If, for example, the mains pressure in the street is 100 kPa, a vertical water lift of about 10 m up the building will result; in practice the minimum head may be about 30 m (294 kPa). Hence for buildings higher than 30 m, some form of pressure boost is required in order for the water to reach the highest point in the building.

Many boosting systems are found in practice; the one most frequently used is the **auto-pneumatic system**, as shown in Figure 1.9. It can be adapted for buildings of various heights.

In this system, the mains water is fed through a ball valve into a break tank. The break tank provides a supply of water, and prevents the pumps from causing a negative pressure on the mains. Duplicate pumps are located after the break tank, but only one of the pumps is in operation at a given

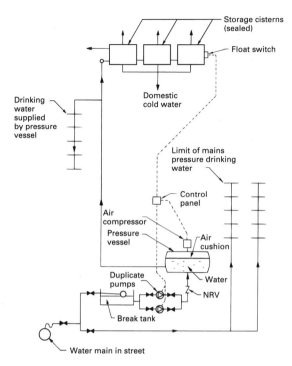

Figure 1.9 Auto-pneumatic system. NRV: non-return valve

time. The other pump is a standby, which will come into operation if the operative one fails.

The pump forces water into a cylindrical horizontal or vertical pressure vessel, and the air compressor imposes an artificial head. The vessel is partially filled with water and has the compressed air cushion above it. The magnitude of the air pressure on the water surface forces the water up to the higher levels.

When water is drawn from the system by a tap being opened, the air expands, causing the pressure to fall. This pressure reduction activates a pressure switch, which is coupled to the pump. This switch operates the pump that supplies the make-up water to the cylinder, compressing the air to a predetermined maximum pressure. The increased pressure on the water surface in the cylinder due to the compressed air then continues to supply the outlets, until the pressure falls once again, and the cycle is repeated.

During operation, some of the air cushion is absorbed into the water, and this has to be replaced, as lack of air pressure would result in continuous operation of the pumps, thus wasting energy. Air make-up is achieved by a sensing float switch in the vessel, which operates the air compressor.

The pressure cylinder has a statutory check by the insurance company once a year, and a sightglass is installed to show the level of the water–air interface.

From Figure 1.9 it may be seen that the drinking water is supplied from the rising main, and only the domestic water for WCs and domestic hot water is supplied from the storage tanks, which may be of the cast iron sectional type. These tanks must conform with the Water Byelaws, by having a sealed lid, filtered breathing pipe and sealed overflow. The storage capacity of these tanks is sized to allow for 24 hours storage. The storage capacity depends on building use, and storage values are given in BS 6700 : 1987 and the CIBSE Guide B4. Typical storage ranges are 120 litres per bedroom for dwelling houses and flats (up to 4 bedrooms), hotels 200 litres per bed, and restaurants 7 litres per meal.

Remember that 1 litre of water weighs 1 kg (also $1 \, m^3 = 1000 \, kg$ or 1 tonne); hence the weight of the water plus the weight of the tank in a large building such as a hotel will impose a very heavy structural load on the roof, and due allowance must be made for this.

PIPE SIZING [9]

The size of the pipe used for the rising main is related to the required flow rate. This required flow is not that which would occur if all the fittings (taps) were open at the same time, but a statistical flow rate based on probability. If a flow related to the maximum (all taps open) was used, the pipe size would be excessive.

Unless a break tank and pneumatic pressure vessel are used, the water pressure at the base of the building will not provide the vertical lift to the ball valve in the tank room.

The pressure of the water in a main entering a building depends on the height of the reservoir (head) above this main. The basic equation used to determine this pressure is:

$$\text{Pressure} = \frac{\text{Force}}{\text{Area}}$$

Hence the pressure due to gravity is

$$\text{Pressure} = \frac{\text{Mass} \times \text{Gravitational constant (9.81 m/s}^2\text{)}}{\text{Area}}$$

where Mass = Volume × Density.

The density of water varies with temperature, and in calculations it is essential to use the exact density. In this case, however, the density is assumed to be 1000 kg/m³, this being the value at 4°C.

Hence the pressure at this temperature produced by a column of water 8 m high is given by

$$\begin{aligned}\text{Pressure} &= 8 \times 1000 \times 9.81 \\ &= 78\ 480\ \text{Pa or } 78.48\ \text{kPa}\end{aligned}$$

So, for water to reach a height of 8 m, it is necessary to have a pressure of 78.48 kPa. In reality, however, frictional resistance of the pipework would reduce this lift.

In domestic low-rise installations, a 15 mm rising main is sufficient to provide an adequate supply of water from the incoming main and overcome the resistance of the ball valve feeding the cistern.

For taller buildings the pipe diameter has to be larger in order to provide the additional water required, and to overcome the extra pipeline and fitting resistance.

Once the water is in the cistern, the flow to the various fittings is by gravity. The pipe size once again reflects the flow rates, which in turn depend on the number of fittings operating (probability). Gravity supplies of cold water in domestic installations are fed to the hot water cylinder and the bathroom sanitary appliances. The supply to the bath is generally 22 mm (dependent on pipe run length) while the wash basin and WC each have a 15 mm supply.

EXAMPLE

The following worked example shows the scope of an answer required in a building services examination paper.

Question

Discuss with the aid of a neat annotated diagram the natural water cycle and the process necessary to supply this water to buildings.

Answer

Figure 1.10 shows the natural water cycle. Warm wind passing over the sea and waterways causes evaporation from the surface. The resulting warm moist air rises to a high level, forming clouds. These clouds are moved by the wind to cooler areas, where

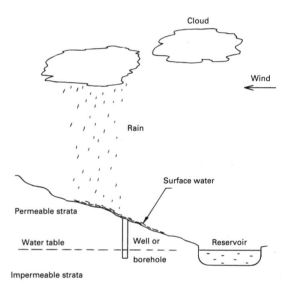

Figure 1.10   The natural water cycle

they reach their dew-point, causing precipitation (rain).

The rain, when it falls on land, passes through permeable strata. The nature of these strata determines whether the water is hard or soft, depending on the amount of dissolved salts that they contain. Excessive hardness prevents soap from lathering, and causes the fouling of heat exchangers. Water treatment will prevent this happening.

The water, on passing through the permeable strata, will collect over the impermeable stratum, from which it may re-emerge as a spring, or form the underground water table. The depths of this table will vary according to the topography and subsoil.

In some areas, wells or boreholes may be used to provide the water supply, although these are suspect as to the water quality, as impurities are picked up as it flows over the ground to the point of extraction. The water from spring-fed rivers or lakes provides a supply that is taken directly to the reservoirs.

After filtration to remove solids and treatment to remove pathogenic bacteria, the water from reservoirs is delivered to the piped networks under the streets. The delivery pressure from the pipe is proportional to the head produced by the height of storage above it, less the losses due to friction. Typical heads are 30–70 m, and these are enough to provide water to the header storage tanks in most buildings. These pressures are also adequate for fire-fighting hydrants, yet at the same time they do not impose excessive strength limits on the piping.

QUESTIONS

1 Discuss the difference between hard and soft water.
2 Describe the operation of the base-exchange method of water treatment.
3 A building has a storage tank located at 70 m above the supply main, in which the water pressure is 500 kPa.
   (a) Will this pressure be sufficient to take water to the storage tank?
   (b) Describe with the aid of sketches how you would overcome a problem of insufficient mains pressure on the upper floors of a building.
4 By means of a neat annotated sketch show all the necessary pipework for direct/indirect systems that is required in a low-rise dwelling.
5 Discuss the reasons for filtering and the sterilization of water as provided to buildings.

In answering some of the above questions, it will be necessary to refer to British Standards publications or the CIBSE Guide, Book B, which cover these topics in greater depth.

REFERENCES

1 Model Water Byelaws (1986)
2 BS 6572 : 1985 *Specification for blue polyethylene pipes for below ground use*
3 BS 6730 : 1986 *Black polyethylene pipes above ground*
4 Ministry of Housing and Local Government *Service cores in high rise flats. Cold water services* Design Bulletin 3 Part 6(1965)
5 BS 1986 : 1953 *Floats for ball valves (copper)*; BS 2456 : 1990 *Floats (plastic) ball valves*
6 Building Regulations 1991 and Approved Documents
7 BS 417 : Part 1 : 1964, Part 2 : 1987 *Galvanized mild steel cistern and covers, tanks and cylinders*
8 BS 2871 : Part 1 : 1971 *Copper tubes for water, gas and sanitation*
9 BS 6700 : 1987 *Specification for design, installation, testing and maintenance of services water for domestic use within buildings and their curtilages*

2 DOMESTIC HOT WATER GENERATION AND DISTRIBUTION

INTRODUCTION

The term **domestic hot water** (DHW) relates to the water supplied for washing purposes.

If the washing process is required for some industrial process, the water may have to be chemically treated in order to protect the process from any salts or metals present in the water supply. In the domestic and commercial field the supply of hot water is normally for body, clothes and dish washing.

In the past, large volumes of hot water were stored in cylinders; this resulted in high running costs due to the heat loss, as well as requiring a considerable floor area to house the cylinder. Today, the trend is to replace such large cylinders with quick-heating, directly fired units.

Care has to be taken in the control of the water temperature. If it is too hot, scalding will result; if it is too cold the risk of legionnaires' disease is increased.

The methods of hot water generation are (see [1]):

- by electric immersion heaters [2];
- by using boilers fired by gas, oil or solid fuel; [3, 4];
- by the use of solar heaters [5].

We shall consider each of these methods in turn.

ELECTRIC IMMERSION HEATERS

The immersion heater is a hollow metal rod with an insulated resistance element inside it. It includes a thermostat, which senses the water temperature: once the water has reached the thermostat temperature setting, the electricity supply is cut off. In this way the water temperature is held at some predetermined level.

The immersion heaters in small domestic cylinders are normally fitted to the top of a well-insulated cylinder (Figure 2.1). It is expensive to heat water

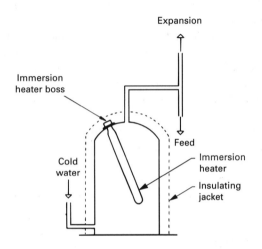

Figure 2.1 A domestic electric immersion heater

with on-peak electricity, so to overcome this problem larger-volume cylinders may be used with an off-peak electricity supply.

In normal domestic systems the electricity supply is single-phase; however, in industrial applications three-phase supply is used.

It will be appreciated from Figure 2.1 that a large volume of water is heated. However, by installating a second immersion heater at a low level with separate switching (Figure 2.2), it is possible to use the small high-level heater, if only water for washing is required, while if a bath has to be run the lower larger unit is used. In this way the cylinder can cope with variable demand.

In order to speed up the installation of domestic hot water systems in residential properties, prefabricated units as shown in Figure 2.3 are sometimes used.

DHW GENERATION BY BOILER SYSTEMS

Domestic hot water may be provided from heat generators in the form of boilers, which may be either direct or indirect.

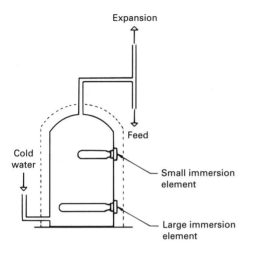

Figure 2.2   A variable-demand electric immersion
heater

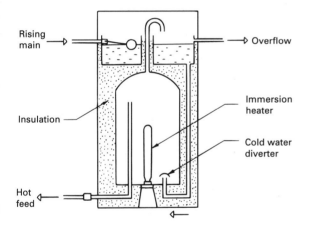

Figure 2.3   A composite plumbing package: electric
hot water heating and cold water
storage

The **direct** method is one in which the storage
of the DHW is reduced to a minimum. The boiler
itself is used only to provide DHW, and is fired
with either gas or oil. This approach reduces the
heat losses to a minimum, resulting in energy saving.

In recent years domestic and small commercial
systems have started to use combination boilers.
These boilers have a dual role, that of providing both
heating and instantaneous hot water. The DHW is
generated from the cold water directly from the main.
This removes the need for the domestic hot water

tank, cylinder and associated pipework. This arrangement saves space and energy, as the heat losses
are reduced to a minimum.

In the past a typical arrangement was similar to
that shown in Figure 2.4, with a heating system
forming part of it. With this arrangement, during the
summer months when heating is not required a larger
boiler than necessary is being used to provide DHW.
A boiler performs at its highest thermal efficiency
when running at maximum demand. Hence with a combined arrangement of this type the seasonal thermal efficiency is low. In commercial installations,
in order to overcome this problem, direct-fired DHW
boilers with low water storage content are used.

Do not confuse the term 'direct fired,' as used
above, with the term 'direct hot water'. Direct firing
relates to the gas being burnt at the point of application, as in an Ascot heater or combi boiler, rather
than in a boiler house some distance away from
the point of draw-off. The term 'direct hot water'
is used to define a system in which the water is
fed from the boiler to the taps or to storage cylinder

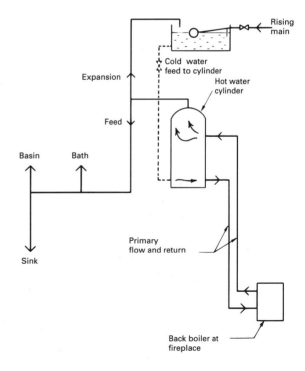

Figure 2.4   Direct hot water generation by open-
fire back boiler

without a heat exchanger in the cylinder. Typical of this type of system is the open fire back boiler system, which was common in residential property built before the Second World War (Figure 2.4).

The disadvantage of the direct system is that mains water from the primary pipework enters the hot water cylinder with each water draw-off. In hard water areas, this leads to furring and the associated restricted flow, with a decrease in the thermal efficiency.

Modern boiler systems use the **indirect** system, in which the primary circuit is a closed circuit: hence the rate of furring up of the pipework is greatly reduced. This arrangement makes use of a heat exchanger inside the hot water cylinder. Hot water circulates through the heat exchanger in the same way as it would through a central heating radiator. The primary flow from the boiler through the heat exchanger may be by gravity (thermosiphonic flow) if the pipe runs are short. In most cases pumped flow is normal; this arrangement is necessary where there are long primary pipe runs.

The heat exchanger [6] is simply a coil of pipe (Figure 2.5) in which the higher-temperature pri-

mary flow inside the tubes transfers heat to the surrounding water.

The primary pipework, heat exchanger and boiler are initially filled with water, for use by that circuit. The cold water tank used for this purpose is known as the **feed and expansion tank** (f & e), and is considerably smaller than the storage tank. An 18 litre feed and expansion tank is suitable for domestic applications, while a typical cold water storage cistern is 230 litres. An example of an indirect domestic hot water system is shown in Figure 2.6.

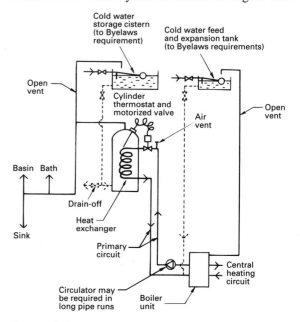

Figure 2.6   Indirect hot water generation

The domestic hot water may be provided from a district heating network, as illustrated in Chapter 4 (Figure 1.28–1.31).

In small systems only a secondary flow is provided; however, in larger systems it is essential to provide a secondary return. This return allows recirculation of the water, ensuring that when a tap is opened, large volumes of cool water do not have to be run off before the hot water reaches the tap. A pipeline without circulation is known as a **dead leg**. The Model Water Byelaws restrict the lengths of the dead legs in order to save on water. The length depends on the pipe diameter; the maximum length of a dead leg in 28 mm copper is 3 m.

The circulation in the pipeline is created by means

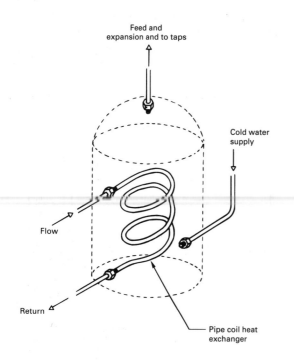

Figure 2.5   An indirect cylinder showing the heat exchanger

of a bronze impeller pump fitted in the secondary return. In the case of internal domestic hot and cold water services, the pipe material normally used is copper. Should steel be used, oxygen bubbles in the water will cause corrosion of the pipework, with the associated discoloration of the water leaving the taps.

POINT–OF–USE DOMESTIC HOT WATER SUPPLY

The domestic hot water systems covered up to now have been fed from a heating boiler, which may receive its heat by the combustion of coal, oil or gas, or by the use of standard or off-peak electricity. These heat-producing sources are remote from the actual point of use, resulting in expensive heat loss in the long runs of flow and return pipework. Another point to consider is the actual quantity and frequency of hot water use at these distant points. In old buildings, large storage cylinders (calorifiers) may still be seen; these represent a heat loss so, by eliminating these cylinders or reducing their size, energy will be saved.

Instantaneous domestic hot water heating units are known as **local** or **direct units,** and use gas or electricity. They are designed to be positioned at or near to the point of maximum use, rather than in a boiler house some distance away.

A typical small direct unit such as an electric shower has no storage provision; it does, however, require a high heat input, to overcome the lack of storage. The storage system, by contrast, allows a small energy input over many hours. The electric instantaneous heaters used in domestic hot water systems have a power consumption of up to 9 kW.

If there are a number of appliances on a pipework run that require a higher water flow rate, a storage cylinder of sufficient capacity is provided at the point of use to take care of the greater water demand. If they feed one appliance they are called **single-point,** while **multi-point** units feed more than one appliance; these have a small storage cylinder of sufficient storage capacity. Such local units are connected direct to the mains water supply, suitable provision being made for pressure reduction and thermal expansion. The electrically heated unit

obviously does not require a flue, whereas the gas-fired unit does.

Gas-fired burners on the direct and storage type are activated when water drawn off from the appliance causes a pressure or temperature drop below a preset level.

PRIMATIC INDIRECT HOT WATER CYLINDER

The indirect method of hot water generation involves an enclosed primary circuit, requiring the use of a small feed and expansion cold water tank, for filling and expansion provision for the primary circuit. This cold water tank requires connections to the rising main as well as provision of unopen vent. If use is made of a cylinder known as a **Primatic** savings can be made by eliminating the pipework and feed and expansion tank.

The cylinder consists of a heat exchanger comprising two chambers, between which an airlock is formed when the system is filled. This arrangement allows the primary circuit to be filled with water taken from within the hot water cylinder. It is essential that the water in the primary circuit (boiler) does not mix with the water in the secondary circuit (to the taps). Figure 2.7 shows how the primary flow is kept from the secondary circuit by means of the air pocket.

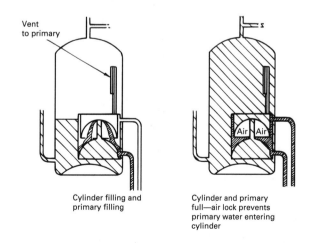

Cylinder filling and primary filling

Cylinder and primary full—air lock prevents primary water entering cylinder

Figure 2.7 Primatic hot water cylinder

UNVENTED HOT WATER SYSTEMS

The provision of domestic hot water by the direct and indirect methods shown in Figures 2.4 and 2.6 has been the accepted practice in the UK. In both these systems the outgoing pipe conveying the hot water from the storage cylinder acts as an open vent over the cold water storage tank. In Europe, however, the unvented system has been used for many years. This system has no venting facility on the cylinder. The Water Byelaws and Building Regulations 1991 and Approved Document G have now made provision for the use of unvented hot water systems in the UK.

The pressures generated in the system by the expansion of water are taken care of by means of an expansion valve and an expansion vessel, as shown in Figure 2.8. Further safety provision is provided with a pressure relief valve on the top of the storage cylinder.

It is essential in using this system that the arrangements and fittings are to the requirements of the Water Byelaws and the Building Regulations [7].

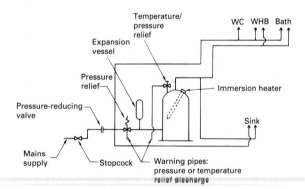

Figure 2.8   The unvented hot water system

DOMESTIC HOT WATER BY SOLAR ENERGY

The use of solar energy for heating purposes is covered in Chapter 4 . The same approach can be used for hot water generation, thus saving on energy. In the UK, however, the pay back in a domestic installation is less than 10 per cent when compared with electric water heating.

A typical arrangement is as shown in Figure 2.9. The solar energy collected by the plate collector is circulated to a storage cylinder. This cylinder must be provided with an auxiliary source of energy, either fossil fuel or electricity, in order to provide hot water during the night or at times of inadequate solar gain.

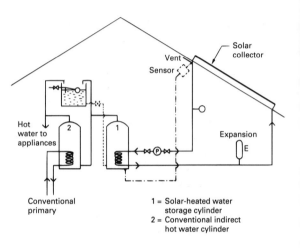

Figure 2.9   Solar generation of hot water

DOMESTIC HOT WATER TEMPERATURE

It has in the past been common practice to store domestic hot water at a temperature of 50–55 °C. This temperature reduces the rate of heat loss from the cylinder and ensures that the water at the tap will not result in scalding. However, to reduce the risk of legionnaires' disease, and kill all bacteria, the storage temperature should be 60 °C.

In residential homes and hospitals the guidelines of the Department of Health must be met, and a water temperature of 60 °C is not allowed at the point of use. The water leaving the tap must be 43 ± 2 °C. As this water temperature is too low to eliminate legionnaires' disease, the water at 60 °C must be blended with cold water at a thermostatic mixing valve to provide the safe leaving water temperature.

QUESTIONS

To provide comprehensive answers to the following questions, students will need to carry out further research.

1   Discuss the advantages and disadvantages of using each of the following methods for the generation of domestic hot water:
    (a)   electric immersion heaters;
    (b)   a combustion system;
    (c)   solar panels.
    It is essential in answering the above that neat sketches are used.

2   What are the advantages of using composite plumbing packages as shown in Figure 2.3?

3   It is suggested to you, that a direct system of domestic hot water is the best system to be installed in your house. Comment on this statement.

4   What is the difference, if any, between an indirect cylinder and a heat exchanger?

5   Describe the operation of a solar panel, as used to generate domestic hot water, stating its advantages and disadvantages.

6   Describe the operation of a Primatic indirect hot water cylinder.

7   What salts are found in domestic hot water systems, and what effect do these have on the operation of the system?

8   In what instance would you use an unvented domestic hot water system?

REFERENCES

1   BS 6700 : 1987 *Specification for design installation testing and maintenance of services supplying water for domestic use within buildings and their curtilages*

2   BS 7671 : 1992 *Requirements for electrical installations* (*Note*: This is the same as the IEE Regulations, 16th Edition.)

3   BS 5258 : Part 1 : 1986 *Safety of domestic gas appliances*; BS 6332 : Part 1 : 1988 *Specification for thermal performance of central heating boilers*

4   BS 5546 : 1990 *Code of practice for installations of gas hot water supplies for domestic premises*

5   BS 5918 : 1989 *Code of practice for solar heating systems for domestic hot water*

6   BS 853 : 1990 *Specification for calorifiers and storage vessels for central heating and hot water supply*

7   BS 6283 : 1991 *Safety devices for use in hot water system*

3 DISPOSAL SERVICES: SANITARY APPLIANCES, DRAINAGE ABOVE AND BELOW GROUND, SOLID WASTE STORAGE

INTRODUCTION

This chapter examines typical forms of sanitary appliances found in property, and the means by which the discharges from sanitary appliances are handled both above and below ground. It also briefly examines provision for the removal of refuse from residential property.

Considerable guidance is given by the Building Regulations concerning the services included in this chapter, and Approved Documents G and H contain invaluable references to complement this text.

SANITARY APPLIANCES [1]

The recommended minimum number of sanitary appliances installed in buildings will be dictated by the building's function. In dwellings, for example, the following basic appliances are recommended by both Building Regulation Approved Document G and BS 6465: a WC, a bath or shower, a sink, and a washbasin. The total number of appliances installed and the frequency of their anticipated use will later determine the capacity of the pipes needed to convey discharges from the appliances to the below-ground drainage system.

The number of occupants of the building will be the predominant factor in the planned provision of sanitary appliances, and tables of empirical data are available to assist the building designer in deciding the number of different forms of appliance.

Although many appliances are easily recognized, there are a number of variations within each type that may be usefully examined.

Water closets (WCs)

There are three main types of WC, depending on the location of the water tank or cistern [2]: high level, low level, and close coupled (Figure 3.1).

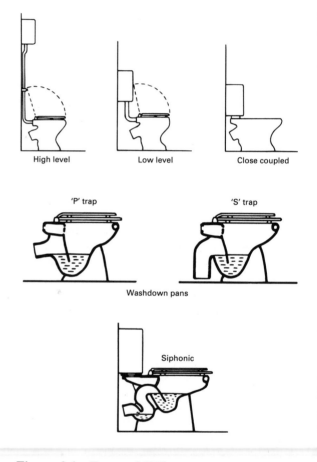

Figure 3.1 Types of WC

High-level WCs are the least acceptable visually for modern domestic use, because of the long flush pipe connecting the cistern to the WC pan. They are, however, very efficient at clearing the contents of the bowl because of the gravitational force created by the lengthy vertical water movement. Both the high-level type and the low-level type use simple washdown pans, as shown in Figure 3.1.

The water retained by the WC pan creates a seal or trap, which prevents foul air from the disposal pipework system from entering the building. For simple washdown pans the style of the trap is similar; the only variation is the direction in which the discharge takes place. In the 'P' trap pan the outlet is fairly close to the horizontal, and this gives an overall 'P' profile to the sectional view. By contrast, where the outlet from the pan is vertical, an 'S' profile is produced.

In the close-coupled arrangement the gravitational force of the water falling from the cistern is relatively small, and assistance to the expulsion of the bowl's contents may be provided by the siphonic action of a siphonic WC pan. This is provided by the outlet channels inside the WC base which, in comparison with those in washdown pans, are narrower and more tortuous. This design encourages siphonic suction forces to develop, and as discharge commences it is this that provides the additional forces to clear the bowl contents. Modern styling of a WC does not mean that the siphonic pan is synonymous with the close-coupled arrangement, and a simple washdown pan may be provided (Figure 3.1).

The various types of WC available are usually made of vitreous china, stainless steel or plastics. Some additional choice of type is provided by WCs that offer a variable flush: short or full. Used as a water-saving device, this could have a marked influence on national water consumption.

Urinals

Vitreous china and stainless steel are the two main materials used for urinals.

Figure 3.2 shows various forms of urinal: stalls, slab, and bowl [3]. Stalls offer a degree of privacy in use, but they occupy more space than the slab type. Bowl urinals are relatively small, and therefore provide the least attendant cleaning commitment, and involve the least initial costs.

Whatever type is installed, there will be provision for washing of the urinal by water, which is usually supplied under gravitational pressure from a water cistern mounted on the wall above. With the stall and bowl urinals this cleaning water is distributed by a spreader on the end of the water supply pipe. With the slab urinal, coverage of the flat face is ensured by the use of a holed sparge pipe, as illustrated in the figure.

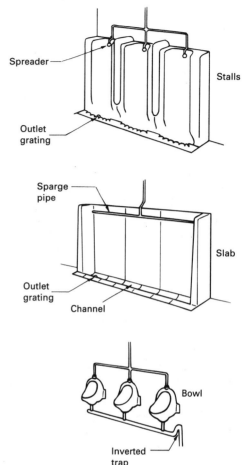

Figure 3.2 Types of urinal

Washbasins

Washbasins are generally made of coloured vitreous china, although stainless steel and acrylics are also available.

Varieties of washbasin arise from the nature of support given to the basin. Figure 3.3 shows three typical forms: the pedestal, bracket and leg, and cantilever. Basins may also be fitted into supporting vanity units or other plastic-laminate-covered surrounds (such as are found in the toilets of motorway services).

In the pedestal basin, the ceramic pedestal that supports the basin is U-shaped in plan and provides a route for the concealment of the hot and

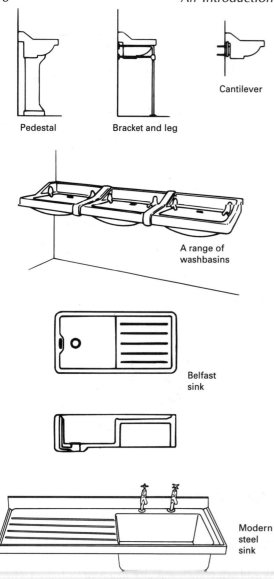

Figure 3.3   Sanitary appliances: washbasins and sinks

an arrangement is generally referred to as a **range** of basins. The overflow facility from basins is generally part of the body of the basin itself, with overspill connected to the waste outlet (Figure 3.3).

Taps provided to basins are usually of the pillar or mixer variety, as in Figure 3.4.

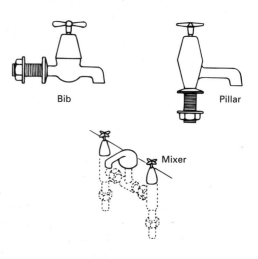

Figure 3.4   Bib, pillar and mixer taps

Sinks

Sinks [4] are used for a variety of purposes, including laundry, culinary, cleaning and laboratory, as well as normal domestic use. The material of the unit normally reflects the nature of the application; glazed fireclay, stainless steel, and glass-reinforced plastics (GRP) are commonly found.

Fireclay tends to be associated with the older and now largely displaced domestic sinks, such as the Belfast type. Cleaner's sinks and laboratory sinks also typically use fireclay, which is very robust for these situations. Figure 3.3 illustrates a Belfast sink and its more modern steel counterpart.

Taps provided are typically the pillar variety, although bib taps, which are attached to the wall rather than the sink itself, are common with cleaner's sinks (see Figure 3.4).

Many household sinks are now provided with an electrical grinder, which can be used to pulverize vegetable peelings and the like for easier disposal

cold water pipes as they are brought up to connect to the taps. Additional stability is provided by screwing this type of basin to the wall.

Where a public facility requires the provision of a number of washbasins, an alternative to the vanity unit type layout is to have basins fixed in close proximity, sometimes with a jointing cover strip of ceramic material between them (Figure 3.3). Such

under water assistance. As a result of the pulp nature of the discharge from the grinder, conventional traps rather than bottle traps (Figure 3.9) should be provided.

Baths

Baths [5] were traditionally formed in cast iron with a porcelain enamelled finish, but nowadays acrylics are preferred, being light and cheaper. The former in its original form was traditionally in rolltop design (Figure 3.5a), but in more recent years a flat-top profile has been adopted irrespective of the materials employed.

As the bath is a large-capacity appliance the water supplies are carried in 22 mm copper pipes, while other appliances only require a 15 mm connection (see Chapters 1 and 2). As a bath should fill in a reasonable time and have a good water supply, there is also the need to install an adequate overflow system. From the bath outlet the usual overflow provision is by a corrugated flexible hose, which connects to the waste trap below the water line (Figure 3.6).

A shortened version of a bath is available in the form of the sitz profile (Figure 3.5b), and this may prove useful in certain circumstances, such as limited space or where the user's mobility is restricted.

DRAINAGE ABOVE GROUND

This section is concerned with the pipework systems that are used to convey the discharges of sanitary appliances down to the below-ground drainage system. These systems are sometimes referred to as **disposal installation pipework** or **waste and soil pipework**.

For the system of pipework to operate efficiently a number of criteria need to be considered in the design [6]. These include the discharge capacity of each appliance connected to the system and the frequency with which each appliance is used. Empirical tables will assist the designer in correct sizing of the pipes and, as might be expected, this is critical in systems provided for larger buildings than domestic. Also, certain appliances cause a large (although momentary) discharge, and this tends to

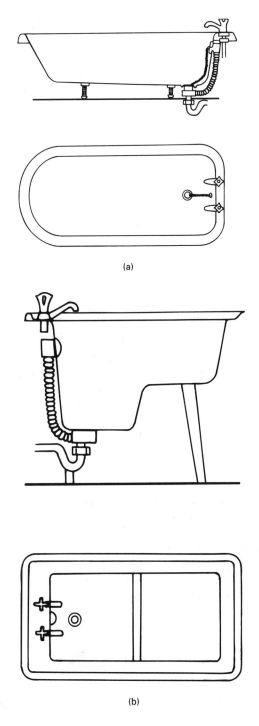

(a)

(b)

Figure 3.5 Baths: (a) rolltop and (b) sitz

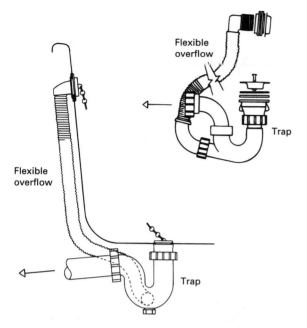

Figure 3.6 Combined trap and overflow to bath

be reflected in the diameter of pipe used to accept the appliance discharge. Flow rates are:

WC	in excess of 2 l/s
bath	about 1 l/s
washbasin	about 0.5 l/s

The diameter of common pipes (such as vertical stacks) is of particular concern to the designer, as allowance must be made for the cumulative effect of all the discharges to be carried. To aid the selection of the correct pipe diameter, a theoretical weighting of **discharge unit values** has been developed. The weighting system reflects the appliance discharge capacity and the likely frequency of use [7]. Some typical discharge unit values for hotel premises are shown below:

Appliance	Frequency of use (minutes)	Discharge unit value
WC (9 litres)	20	7
bath	30	18
washbasin	10	3

By adding the discharge unit values for all of the

appliances connected to a stack, a suitable stack diameter can be taken from tabulated data.

Flow pattern and air pressure fluctuations

When reference is made to pipes conveying discharges from sanitary appliances, two classifications of pipe were formulated with the older discharge systems:

- **waste pipes**: conveying waterbound discharges from sinks, baths, showers, washbasins and bidets;
- **soil pipes**: conveying human discharges from WCs or urinals.

In modern disposal pipework systems these two classes of pipe are combined in a single system.

If we examine the way in which discharges move in these pipes, the flow pattern may be readily visualized where the pipe is close to horizontal. Here, as would be expected, the liquid gravitates to the lowest part of the pipe and fills part of the pipe bore (Figure 3.7). Less easily appreciated is the pattern experienced where pipes are vertical; here the liquid tends to cling to the pipe walls.

In pipework design, consideration needs to be given to the development of pressure within the system. This pressure can take two forms: **positive compression** and **negative suction**. The strongest effects of pressure arise when the bore of the pipe is completely filled, and this is therefore a condition that should be avoided.

Where a near-horizontal pipe has a bore completely filled by the flow the name given to the condition is a **hydraulic jump formation** (Figure 3.8). The flow moves along like a liquid bullet, compressing and displacing the air in front of it and creating negative pressure (suction) behind.

When full-bore flow occurs in a vertical pipe the effect is termed a **plug formation**. In this case, the best analogy is to a cycle pump. The moving liquid disc provides the same effect as the washer in the cycle pump, compressing and displacing the air in front of it and causing negative pressure behind.

The significance of these pressure variations is revealed by examination of their effect on the traps provided to sanitary appliances.

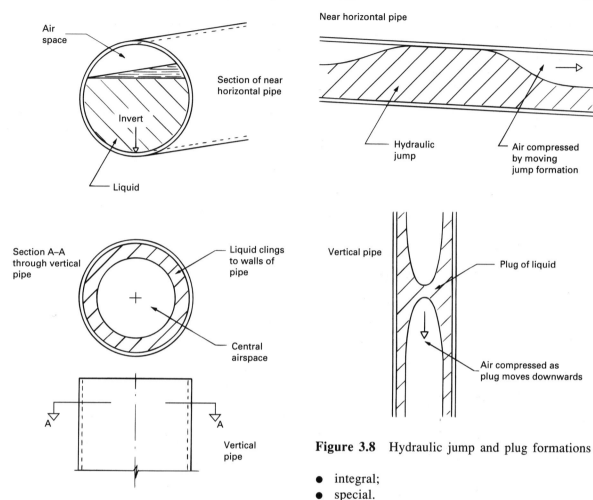

Figure 3.7 Flow patterns in near-horizontal and vertical pipes

Figure 3.8 Hydraulic jump and plug formations

The primary function of the trap is to form a seal against foul air in the pipework system, thus preventing it from entering the building [8]. The trap achieves this by retaining some of the liquid that is discharged by the appliance that it serves. Depths of liquid seal are generally 75 mm, the minimum being 50 mm. The arrangement for liquid retention provides the difference in the style of trap, and a range of types can be listed:

- conventional;
- bottle;
- integral;
- special.

Conventional traps are formed from a series of bends in the pipe, and allow full pipe bore flow through the trap. This trap requires sufficient space to accommodate the various bends; these are arranged to give a 'P' or 'S' profile, depending on the direction of the trap outlet (Figure 3.9).

In contrast the **bottle trap** is more compact: it provides excellent access for the clearance of debris, usually by simply unscrewing the base of the trap body. The working principle of the bottle trap does, however, cause disruption to the smoothness of the flow through the trap, which may prevent its use in certain situations (for example, where sink grinders are to be used).

The WC has a trap in the body of the appliance itself, which is therefore classified as an **integral**

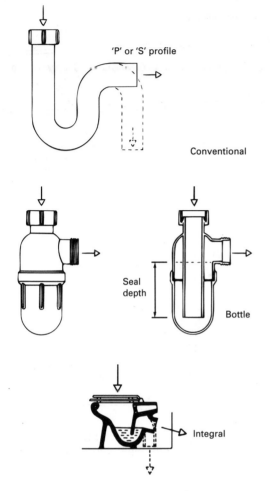

'P' or 'S' profile

Conventional

Seal depth

Bottle

Integral

Figure 3.9   Types of trap

tions created by the flow. Figures 3.10 and 3.11 demonstrate the development of air compression and suction, the latter usually being responsible for movement of the liquid seal in the trap.

Figure 3.10 shows the siphonage of the liquid trap seal resulting from the condition of **self-siphonage**. Such an effect may be expected when the incorrect pipe diameter has been selected: for example, a 32 mm bore pipe to a bath rather than the minimum 38 mm needed. The figure shows a hydraulic jump formation in the flow, which allows the development of a suction zone of negative pressure and removes liquid from the trap.

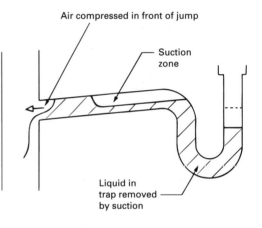

Air compressed in front of jump

Suction zone

Liquid in trap removed by suction

Figure 3.10   Self-siphonage in a waste pipe

trap. As explained earlier, the shape of the outlet and trap provide the distinction between different WC types ('P' and 'S' trap washdown pans).

Special traps provide a particular special function, such as resistance to siphonage action (as in Figure 3.14), or perhaps the interception of components of a waste discharge such as may be needed for laboratory sinks.

Foul air is prevented from entering the premises by the water seal in the trap, and careful thought needs to be given to the preservation of this liquid seal. The occurrence of undesirable discharge flow patterns in the form of hydraulic jump and plug formations may destabilize or even completely destroy the trap seal by the effect of pressure varia-

Figure 3.11 shows suction forces again having an adverse effect on the trap seal, but this time the development of suction is due to flows from other sanitary appliance discharges, which have entered the vertical stack pipe further up the property. These discharges have caused a plug formation, which rushes past the waste branch to the affected appliance, compressing air in front of it and creating negative pressure in its wake. Such an effect is inducing disturbance of the appliance trap seal, and the description given to the condition is **induced siphonage**.

A number of measures may be taken to avoid the effect of air pressure fluctuations on the liquid retained by traps. Self-siphonage may be avoided by using the correct pipe diameter to suit the appliance served. Induced siphonage may be prevented

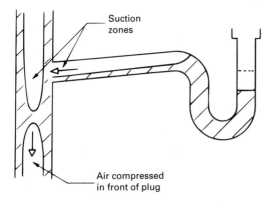

Figure 3.11 Induced siphonage in a waste pipe

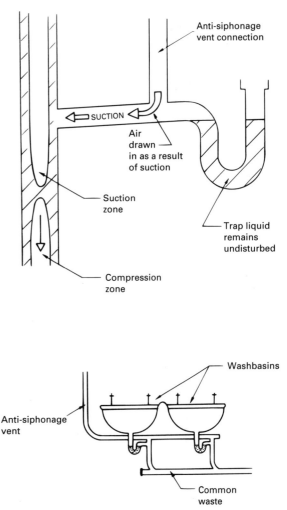

Figure 3.12 Pressure equalization by the use of anti-siphonage pipework

by using a stack of a diameter that discourages the creation of plug formations; alternatively steps may be taken to equalize air pressure fluctuations as they arise, thereby preventing disturbance of the liquid seal in the trap. Such steps include the provision of anti-siphonage ventilation pipework [9], or the use of anti-siphonage traps.

The principle of anti-siphonage ventilation pipework is illustrated in Figure 3.12. By connecting a ventilation source to the waste pipe between the stack and the trap, any suction effects can be nullified by drawing in air from the vent connection. This will of course mean additional cost in the provision of the vent pipework, which sometimes extends through the building into the open air beyond roof level. Once the top floor is reached an alternative route for the ventilation may be by a loop connection to the stack, as shown in Figure 3.13.

Special forms of bottle trap can also be used as a source of fresh air entry, to allow **one-way** movement of air through the trap. The seal against foul air entry to the building is preserved once the air pressure is stabilized by the injection of air (Figure 3.14).

When appliances are connected to a vertical stack, there are often a number of connections to be made on one floor, and bathroom appliances tend to be grouped together. If a waste pipe connection from an appliance is made to the stack directly opposite the soil connection from the WC this would inevitable cause an induced siphonage effect and possibly a loss of seal in the trap served by the waste

pipe. To prevent this the waste pipe may be diverted away from the immediate vicinity of the WC discharge, as shown in Figures 3.15 and 3.16.

The material entering a vertical stack has eventually to change direction at the foot of the stack where the flow enters the below-ground drainage system. At what is effectively almost a right-angle variation in flow direction, there is inevitably going to be turbulence in the material being conveyed, and this in itself can lead to a build-up of pressure within the drain at this point.

Figure 3.17 shows the possible effect of the pressure increase within the pipes, and the possible effect

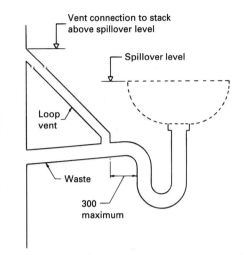

Figure 3.13 Branch ventilation by loop connection to the stack

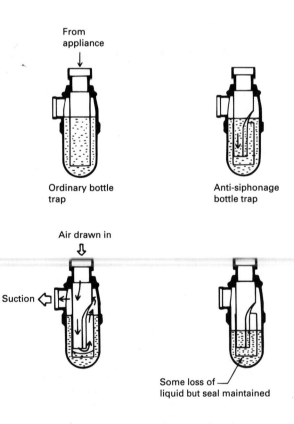

Figure 3.14 The principle of the anti-siphonage bottle trap

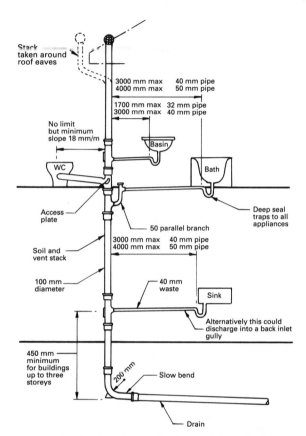

Figure 3.15 Single-stack disposal installation

that this may have on any waste pipe connected close to the base of vertical stack pipes, where a major change occur in the direction of the flow. Pressurized foul air is entering the waste branch, partly displacing the liquid retained in the trap to the appliance, and some of the foul air is percolating through the trap liquid.

To prevent this occurrence careful thought should be given to the vertical distance between the base of the stack at the change of direction, and the point of the waste connection to the stack as shown.

Waste and soil pipework connections

From the variety of different pipework arrangements possible for the collection of discharges from sanitary appliances, there are three major classifications:

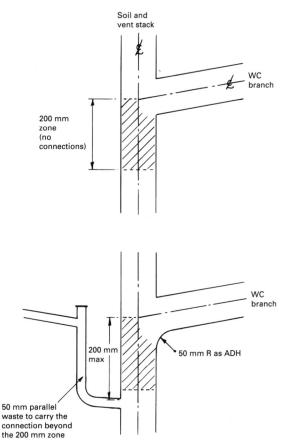

Figure 3.16 Stack connections to avoid siphonage

- single-stack system;
- one-pipe system;
- two-pipe system.

Single stack is a solution employed extensively in domestic housing, and a typical layout is shown in Figure 3.15. The stack in this arrangement may be located inside or outside the external wall of the property, and terminates above roof eaves level with a cage or perforated cover. At this point the stack acts as a means of ventilating the below-ground drainage system, which commences at the base of the stack.

As detailed, the waste pipe from the kitchen sink may be connected to the stack, but it may also be connected directly to a drain gully. Many older properties have kitchen waste pipes that discharge

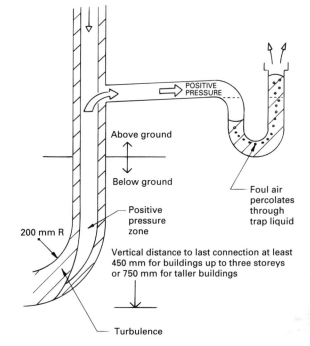

Figure 3.17 Back-pressure percolation

over the grating of a drain gully; this usually leads to the accumulation of solids on top of the grating. Current Building Regulations require the discharge from the waste pipe to enter the gully below grating level but above the water retained by the gully (back inlet gully as illustrated later in Figure 3.23).

Other features of the single-stack system are deep seal traps on waste pipes (75 mm minimum seal) and restrictions on the length of waste and soil pipe connections to the stack, as shown in Figure 3.15. On occasion it may be necessary to incorporate anti-siphonage ventilation pipework as previously discussed, particularly if a single stack is chosen as the disposal system for a multi-storey building.

The **one-pipe system** (Figure 3.18), by contrast, is a fully ventilated arrangement. Note the anti-siphonage connections throughout [10].

It is often said that the relatively large discharge from the WC is most influential in the development of air pressure fluctuations in the disposal installation, despite the fact that it is only a momentary discharge. The **two-pipe system** separates the WC discharges by using two collecting stacks: a **soil stack** for collection of the discharges from

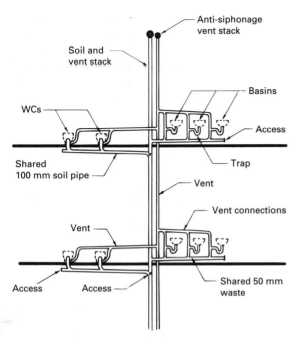

Figure 3.18   One-pipe disposal installation

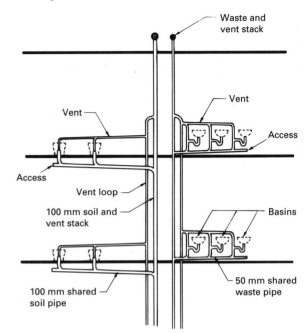

Figure 3.19   Two-pipe disposal installation

the WC, and a **waste stack** for collection of the water-bound waste discharges from the other appliances (Figure 3.19).

Selection of one of the disposal arrangements in preference to another is usually based on a number of criteria, of which the proposed layout of the appliances on each floor and the distance of the appliances to the stack are probably the most influential. Provided that careful design is employed and appliances are grouped around the stack, the economical single-stack system may be chosen for high-rise as well as low-rise structures.

Where the cumulative effect of discharges is such that siphonage effects could develop, and this is particularly the case for multi-storey buildings, a one-pipe or two-pipe system may be preferable.

DRAINAGE BELOW GROUND

In the design of above-ground drainage systems a division of discharge was sometimes made into **waste discharges** and **soil discharges**. In below-ground

drainage both waste and soil discharges enter the **foul drain** and are separated from the rainwater collected, the latter being carried by the **surface water drain**, where a dual system operates.

To remove doubt as to the contents of a foul drain, students should remember that this takes discharges from all sanitary appliances.

When examining below-ground drainage systems there are three main classifications that apply:

- the combined system;
- the separate system;
- the partially separate system.

In the **combined system**, rainwater and sanitary appliance discharges are carried together in a single pipe. This may be economic in terms of minimizing pipe lengths, but it places an unnecessary burden on the sewage treatment works, in that rainwater does not require treatment. Many older existing developments have combined arrangements of below-ground drainage, but the more modern and environmentally acceptable solution is to provide a **separate system**, which recognizes the benefits of isolating rainwater. **Partially separate systems** carry rainwater from public areas such as roads and pavements in the surface water drain, while all or most of the rainwater collected from private premises is discharged into the foul drain, together with the sanitary appliance discharges. Such arrangements may allow the use of the terms **public** and **private** drainage.

Other terms to be noted include the meaning of **drain, private sewer**, and **public sewer**. These are illustrated in Figure 3.20.

From a design point of view there are a number features that, if incorporated into below-ground drainage systems, should assist the efficiency of operation:

(1) Pipe layouts should be simple, with as few changes in direction or gradient as possible.
(2) Pipe runs should be in straight lines.
(3) The system should be ventilated (usually through the stack pipe of the above-ground drainage system).

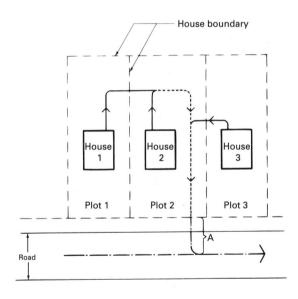

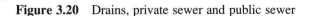

——— Drain

------- Private sewer

—·—·— Public sewer

A   Public sewer if adopted by Local Authority following the Public Health Act 1936, otherwise private sewer

Figure 3.20   Drains, private sewer and public sewer

(4) Pipes should be laid at a depth in the ground to avoid damage, or specially protected if shallow.
(5) Pipe gradients should suit the material being conveyed (flows containing solids and liquids should achieve a **self-cleansing velocity**).
(6) The pipes should have a capacity to suit the anticipated peak flow.
(7) The pipe materials used should suit the type of discharge being conveyed (whether hot or aggressive, for example) and the prevailing ground conditions (for example, if contaminated).
(8) Pipe joints must be watertight; flexible joints, which are now the norm, will generally allow a 5° distortion between pipes without breaking the joint seal.
(9) Suitable bedding should be used below the pipes and suitable backfill around the pipes [11].
(10) Sufficient points for access should be provided (for inspection or the clearing of blockages).
(11) Junctions to the main flow should be minimized and should be made in the direction of the main flow.
(12) Entries to the drain should be trapped (except the entry at the base of the above-ground drainage stack, which is the means by which the below-ground drain is ventilated).

Adherence to this list should provide a system that requires little maintenance.

In conveying its contents to the point of termination, perhaps the local authority sewer, the drain should achieve a self-cleansing velocity. The provision of a suitable gradient to the pipe will dictate the depths of the drainage trenches and the overall economy of the excavation.

When sizing the pipe diameters needed for the foul drain, an estimate may be made of the extent of flows emanating from the sanitary appliances served, but sizing of the surface water drains can be more difficult. In this case the size may relate to:

● the catchment area of the ground from which rainwater is to be collected;

- the likely intensity of rainfall over this area (perhaps assessed by reference to Meteorological Office records);
- consideration of the permeability/impermeability of the ground within the catchment area;
- the gradient of the pipe diameter proposed, which will determine the flow velocity and the rate of flow.

BS 8301 *Code of Practice for Building Drainage* contains a number of tables to assist in the correct sizing of drain pipes (see also Figure 3.21).

Of particular use are:

- Table 4: flow rates, probability of discharge factors, and discharge unit ratings;
- Figure 1: probability graph for number of appliances discharging simultaneously;
- design flows for foul drains: conversion of discharge units to flow rates (see also Figure 3.21)

This background information to the design of drainage systems is now discussed under the headings of inlets to the drain; access; pipe materials, jointing and bedding; and drain termination.

Inlets to the drain: gullies and traps

Most drain runs will commence immediately outside the building perimeter, so to prevent foul air from the drain escaping into the air around the building an effective **gully** detail is employed. The liquid seal that results from the use of a gully is formed by a bend in the same way as previously discussed for use in traps to sanitary appliances.

Traditionally, the gully is a one-piece detail with a fixed direction of outlet, but as shown in Figure 3.22 a two-piece gully has the advantage of manoeuvrability, in that its trap may be rotated to suit the desired direction of the drain run that is to follow.

Rainwater pipes often discharge their contents over the grating of the gully, as do the waste pipes of older above-ground drainage systems. Recognizing that the latter practice may result in the accumulation of sediment/solids on top of the grating, the current Building Regulations require waste pipes to discharge their contents below grating level but above the trap water level [12]. A **back inlet gully**, as shown in Figure 3.23, is the normal way of

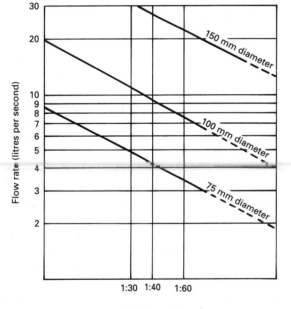

Figure 3.21   Drain flow rates

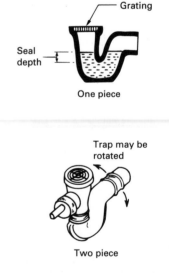

Figure 3.22   One– and two-piece gullies (two-piece gully courtesy of Hepworth Iron Co. Ltd)

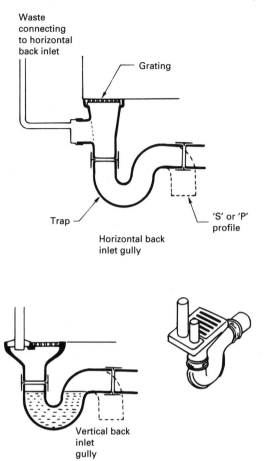

Figure 3.23 Horizontal and vertical back inlet gullies

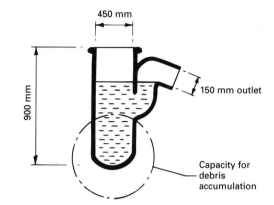

Figure 3.24 A typical road gully

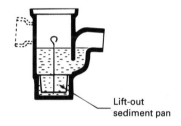

Figure 3.25 A mud-intercepting gully

satisfying the needs of the Building Regulations. This can have either a horizontal or a vertical back inlet facility.

The same basic principle of forming a water seal against foul air movement is employed in the larger road gully detail (Figure 3.24). Note on this the 150 mm outlet diameter, compared with the 100 mm outlet from ordinary gullies, and the capacity to allow sediment collection without affecting the function of the gully.

Special gullies are available that have an intercepting role: for sediment or for petrol, for example. Figure 3.25 shows a **mud gully**, which has a lift-out sediment pan and the capacity to collect a quantity of material without affecting the normal water route.

The **petrol/oil interceptor** is often employed to serve the water collected from the forecourt of petrol filling stations, which is likely to be polluted with petrol and oil spillage (Figure 3.26). This works on the principle that petrol, being less dense than water, will float on the surface of water and evaporate. By carrying the petrol-contaminated discharge through a series of chambers, which have an overspill connection well below their water line, a less contaminated flow progresses from one chamber to the next. As vaporization of petrol is expected, a system of vent pipes is connected to each chamber to carry the petrol vapour to a safe place for discharge into the open air.

The detail illustrated shows traditional brick and *in-situ* concrete construction. Such chambers are also available in pre-formed glass-reinforced plastic (GRP); these are quicker to install and better suited to difficult ground conditions.

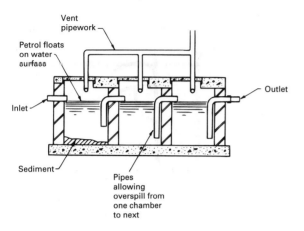

Figure 3.26   A petrol interceptor

Access to the drain

Access may be provided to the drain by:

- manholes;
- inspection chambers;
- rodding eyes;
- rodable gullies

Traditionally constructed **manholes** consist of brick-work and concrete, as shown in Figure 3.27. This shows the common practice of exposing the flow as it enters the chamber by the use of a half-section pipe, referred to as a **channel**. Any spillage is re-directed towards the channel by the surrounding concrete benching. This detail clearly shows the **invert level**, which is of fundamental importance in the design of the drainage system, in ensuring the provision of the correct falls to the pipes.

The invert level refers to the lowest part of the flow. This could be the lowest part of the channel in a manhole detail, or indeed the lowest part of the internal bore of a pipe at any position. Invert level is a statement of the level of the flow relative to ordnance datum. All measurements are relative to a base-point zero, which is mean sea level at Newlyn, Cornwall. This provides the basis on which the height of the land (contours) or land features such as mountains are measured. It is also the basis on which the depth of the sea is measured.

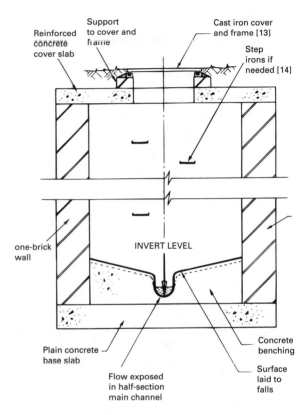

Figure 3.27   Traditional brick manhole

Manholes are not only used to inspect the flow but are positioned at points where flows are brought together, as such points are the site of potential blockages [15]. To assist the turning of incoming connections towards the general direction of the main flow, special three-quarter-section branch bends are used (Figure 3.28). Whenever possible, branches should join the main flow in the same direction as the main flow but, as illustrated, obtuse connections may be handled by the branch bend.

Where manholes are shallow details of less than about 2 m invert depth (measured from cover level to the invert level), the sectional shape of the chamber will be similar to that shown on the left in Figure 3.29. However, beyond this depth it would not be economic to maintain the chamber dimensions from the base up to the cover. As shown in

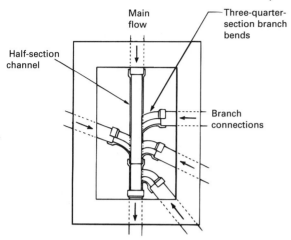

Figure 3.28 Branch connections at the manhole

Figure 3.29, the deeper manhole may be constructed in two distinct parts: the **access shaft** and the **working chamber**. Note the need for an intermediate reinforced concrete slab to accommodate the changes in dimension.

Internal dimensions of manholes will vary, not only with depth, but also with the numbers of in-coming branch connections. BS 8301 suggests minimum plan dimensions of 1200 × 750 mm for manholes generally, with deeper chambers served by an access shaft of at least 900 × 840 mm.

As a guide to the plan length of a chamber, an allowance of up to 375 mm may be made for each incoming 100 mm diameter branch, and up to 500 mm for each incoming 150 mm branch.

Another function may be provided by the manhole, namely connecting drain flows that are at different depths in the ground (different depths to invert). A **backdrop manhole** (Figure 3.30) may also be used to absorb vertical distances as the flow from the building moves towards the point of termination. This allows desirable gradients to be achieved with the pipe between successive backdrop details, ensures the preservation of a self-cleansing velocity for the flow, and avoids excessive excavation.

As illustrated, the backdrop manhole will contain not only a section of vertical pipework but also typically a tumbling bay facility, which allows for extreme flow situations. This feature can also allow

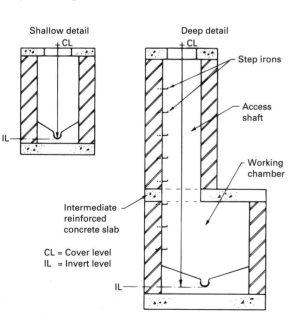

Figure 3.29 Shallow and deep manhole profiles

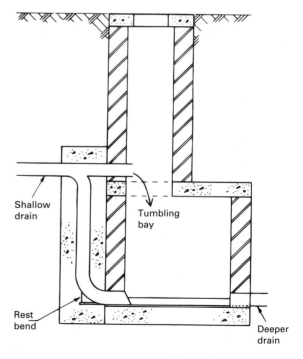

Figure 3.30 Backdrop manhole

access for rodding blockages that occur in the shallower drain.

In addition to the traditionally constructed *in-situ* brickwork manholes, a preformed alternative is available in the form of precast concrete, which is particularly well suited for deep manholes. The interior arrangement of channels and branches for these chambers may be formed on site but is also obtainable preformed. The premoulded base can be ordered by using a schedule (Figure 3.31), which shows the required size and the number of connections. The preformed base is cast with its upper surface to falls to direct any spillage into the channel and branches.

Inspection chambers may be constructed of the same materials as manholes but are physically smaller units. Strictly speaking, a manhole should contain a chamber that has a volume capable of accommodating an operative to allow inspection or rodding of the flow. For the inspection chamber the intention is to inspect or clear blockages from ground level (Figure 3.32).

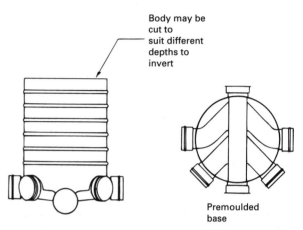

Figure 3.32 A plastics inspection chamber (courtesy of Hunter Plastics Ltd)

Another access possibility is the **rodding eye** (Figure 3.33). This is typically used as an alternative to a chamber detail where flows come together and the potential for blockage exists. A removable plate forms the sealed end to the pipe; this is generally set in a block of concrete. Note the use of a slow bend to bring the drain up to ground level.

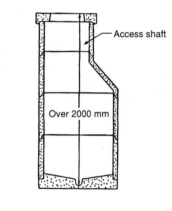

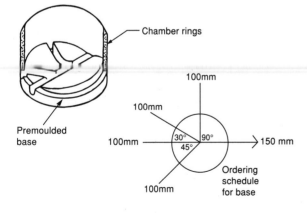

Figure 3.31 Precast concrete manhole, and ordering schedule [16]

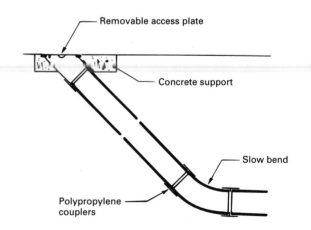

Figure 3.33 A rodding eye detail (courtesy of Hepworth Iron Co. Ltd)

For many years the tortuous route through gullies has prevented their use as a source of access to the drain. However, a gully is now available that has a removable interior, allowing free access for rodding. This works on the principle of a bottle trap. It is manufactured by Wavin Plastics, with the range name of Osmadrain (see Figure 3.34).

Pipe materials, jointing and bedding

Clay pipes have been used in below-ground drainage for many decades. In their original form the naturally porous material was rendered impervious by the process of salt glazing, and the pipes were referred to as **salt glazed ware**. More recent developments in the manufacture of drainage products have revolutionized the process of sealing the material, and the technique applied now is vitrification.

Although visually the vitrified pipe appears porous (very dull, matt finish), the internal characteristics of the pipe have been changed and become glass-like under the effects of the heat treatment process.

Clay pipes and fittings are produced to the BS 65 quality standard [17], which allows jointing to take place in a number of ways. Socket-and-spigot joints are traditional, but plain-ended pipes can be used, which have special polypropylene joints (Figure 3.35).

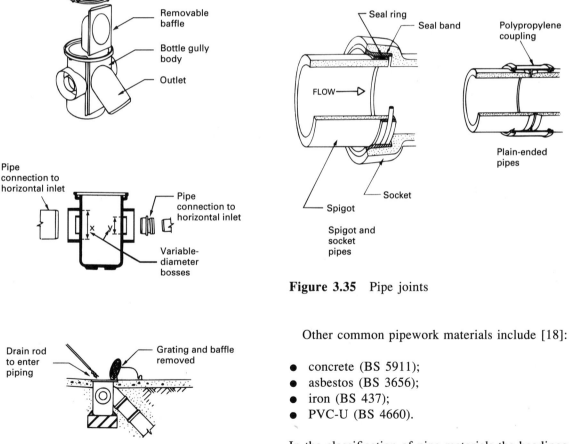

Figure 3.35 Pipe joints

Other common pipework materials include [18]:

- concrete (BS 5911);
- asbestos (BS 3656);
- iron (BS 437);
- PVC-U (BS 4660).

In the classification of pipe materials the headings **rigid** and **flexible** are generally used. The choice of one of these may be dictated by a number of factors, including the need to resist deformation under

Figure 3.34   A roddable gully (courtesy of Wavin Plastics Ltd – Osmadrain)

load. Rigid pipes such as clay do not deform under load; this particular form of rigid pipe is supplied in three strengths to suit varying conditions. Clay, a naturally available material, also performs well against chemicals, impurities, and high-temperature flows.

Table 3 of BS 8301 should be consulted for more specific information concerning the performance of different pipe materials.

Irrespective of the pipe material chosen, there are also two forms of pipe joint, which may be classified using the same system employed for the pipes themselves, **rigid** and **flexible**. Figure 3.36 shows some rigid and flexible pipe joints.

A normal feature of the flexible joint is its ability to allow a 5° distortion between one pipe and the next while maintaining a liquid seal at the joint. Other advantages of the flexible joint are as follows:

- Flexible joints are dry joints, and this means that the drain can be tested immediately on completion.
- Less skill is required in forming the joint, and consequently jointing is quicker.
- Poor weather does not interrupt laying.

The bedding given to drainage pipes will have a marked influence on the overall strength of the pipe run. Concrete provides traditional support to pipes, but granular beds and supports are now more frequently applied, particularly with flexibly jointed pipes.

Concrete support is often associated with high ground load situations, and support may take varying forms using beds, beds and haunchings, or beds and surrounds (Figure 3.37). Special detailing may

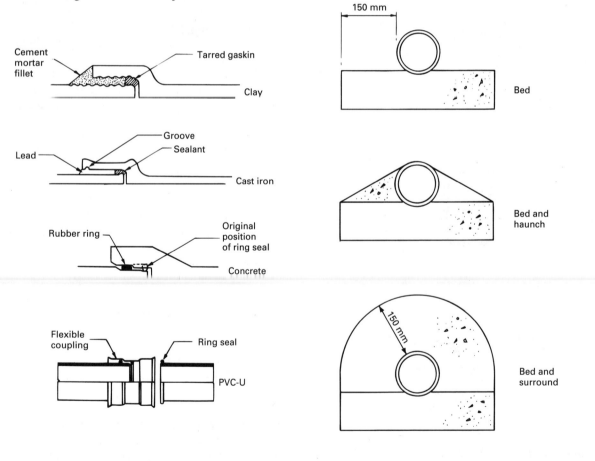

Figure 3.36   A selection of rigid and flexible joints

Figure 3.37   Traditional concrete supports to pipes

apply when movement of the ground is anticipated (Figure 3.38a).

Granular alternatives may be used with both rigid and flexible pipes, and again special details are suggested for situations where ground movement is expected (Figure 3.38b).

Drain termination

The introduction to this chapter considered the populated environment, where drains from the buildings discharged into public sewers for conveyance to the treatment works. However, less populated areas may not be served by public sewers, and alternative means of termination may be needed.

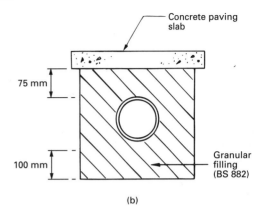

(b)

Figure 3.38 Drain support where ground movement is anticipated: (a) movement joint in concrete pipe encasement; (b) granular encasement for flexible pipe

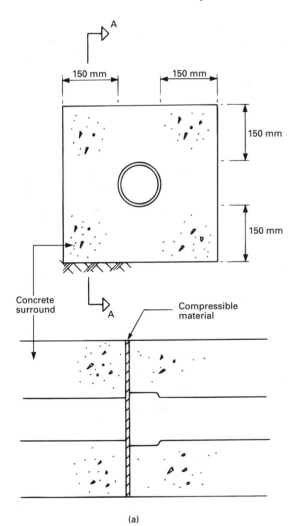

(a)

The two main options in such circumstances would be to provide a holding facility from where the public authority could remove the material periodically (such as a cesspool), or to provide some treatment of the material before discharging locally (a septic tank, for example).

It is estimated that a three-person household will generate 7 m³ of discharge in three weeks, and the holding capacity of a **cesspool** [19] needs to reflect this, as well as the frequency of collecting anticipated. The Building Regulations 1991 [20] recommend a minimum capacity of 18 m³, and BS 6297 suggests that the design should accommodate at least 45 days' discharge.

Cesspools may be of traditional engineering brick construction with a concrete base and reinforced cover slab in the style of a traditionally constructed manhole, but this is often superseded by pre-formed construction in GRP (glass-reinforced plastic) (Figure 3.39).

There will need to be a fresh air inlet to the cesspool, and also a ventilation pipe for the release of generated gases. Positioning of the cesspool needs to consider the likely odours emerging from the tank and also the need for access for the emptying tanker. It is desirable that at least 15 m is maintained from the building while keeping within 30 m of a vehicle access road.

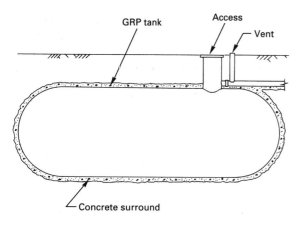

Figure 3.39 Cesspool (courtesy of Conder Tanks)

Where there is a single residential property or a small group of them not served by a public sewer some elementary treatment of the sewage may be provided before discharge by using a **septic tank** installation [21].

As with the cesspool the capacity of this tank needs to be carefully assessed. The Building Regulations 1991 recommend a minimum capacity of 2700 litres, while BS 6297 prescribes 2720 litres. The latter reference also provides the following formula for determining capacity based on the number of persons served:

$$C = (180P + 2000) \text{ litres}$$

where C = capacity and P = the number of persons.

As sewage passes through the tank the flow is retarded by passage through successive chambers (usually two). During this process, partial purification occurs as a result of the generation of anaerobic bacteria, in which methane gas, sludge, and liquid are the by-products. Sludge accumulation will necessitate removal, typically on a six-month basis.

Construction of the septic tank may be of traditional brick and concrete but again, as with the cesspool, GRP and other materials are available (Figure 3.40), as illustrated and described in *Building Technology* by Seeley [22]. Seeley also shows both three-stage upward flow and a nitrification small sewage treatment plant.

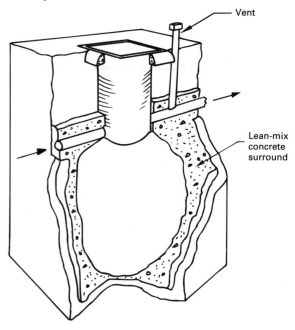

Figure 3.40   Septic tank (courtesy of Conder Tanks)

For a greater degree of treatment than is achievable with the septic tank, a biological **filter** of granular material may be used in a tank similar to those found at a sewage treatment works.

Incoming material is spread over the surface of the granular filter by mechanical tumbling plates or by rotating distribution pipes. When the material has passed down through the tank it reaches the sloping base of the tank, which directs the residue to the point of outlet (Figure 3.41).

Material leaving the filter bed may be subject to further treatment through a humus tank, which collects the bacterial residue, or, if environmentally acceptable, the outflow may be simply distributed on the surrounding land through a suitable land drainage system or into a watercourse.

REFUSE DISPOSAL

When considering the system to be employed for the collection of refuse there are a number of points to be considered:

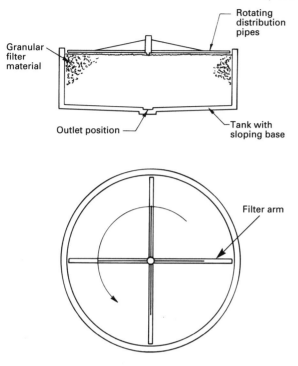

Rotating distribution pipes

Granular filter material

Outlet position

Tank with sloping base

Filter arm

Figure 3.41 Filtration

- the nature of the waste (perishable or unperishable);
- the nature of the premises generating the waste (domestic, industrial, commercial);
- the location of the point of generation (height from the ground, position on the floor layout).

The waste generated by dwellings is a primary source of refuse, and the nature of this material has changed over the past two decades. The material collected is now lighter and more bulky than before, perhaps reflecting the extent of the use of plastics and the much-reduced number of solid-fuel-burning appliances.

As the nature of the waste generated by industrial and commercial premises is often special, it is the intention of this section to concentrate on the material generated by residential premises.

The geometry of the premises served by refuse collection will have a considerable influence on the design of the collection method, and height is particularly influential. The Building Regulations outline the need for refuse chutes to serve properties over four storeys high, as the manual collection of refuse from tall structures would be inconvenient and inefficient.

Code of Practice 306 previously helped to define the types of container that could be used to store refuse, and this has subsequently been refined by BS 5906 [23]:

- **individual refuse containers** (such as dustbins not exceeding 0.12 m³ capacity);
- **communal waste storage containers** (0.75–1 m³ capacity);
- **bulk waste containers** (1–30 m³ capacity).

Solid waste disposal systems

Figure 3.42 summarizes the various methods for the collection and disposal of solid waste from residential premises.

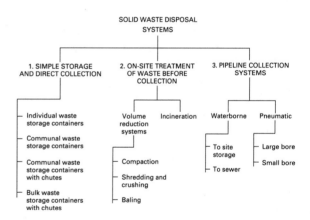

Figure 3.42 Solid waste disposal systems

The depositing of refuse manually by residents into various sizes of container has already been mentioned as a satisfactory method for buildings of no more than four storeys. For taller buildings, however, a **refuse chute** [24] may present an efficient method of disposal. The components of a typical chute are shown in Figure 3.43.

The chute needs to be smooth and impervious internally, and constructed of incombustible material for safety in the event of fire. Suitable materials for the interior of a chute include clay or concrete pipes,

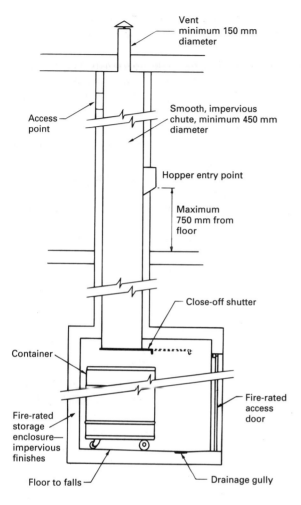

Vent minimum 150 mm diameter

Access point

Smooth, impervious chute, minimum 450 mm diameter

Hopper entry point

Maximum 750 mm from floor

Close-off shutter

Container

Fire-rated access door

Fire-rated storage enclosure—impervious finishes

Floor to falls

Drainage gully

Figure 3.43   The component parts of a refuse chute

On-site treatment of waste

When refuse collection systems involve large volumes of material it may be considered viable to install a means of reducing the volume of material and thereby increasing the intervals between removal from site. Such volume reduction can be achieved by compacting, shredding, baling, or incinerating the refuse.

Automatic turntables with rotating collection sacks may be considered, for example, for installation at the base of refuse chutes. If these rotating turntables have the benefit of ram compactors a double benefit will be achieved. The ram will compact the material in the collection sacks, and a reduction of approximately 4 to 1 may be expected. The combined effect of increasing the number of sacks by using a turntable arrangement and having on-site compaction will have a dramatic influence on the collection period for refuse removal.

Incineration can achieve even more efficiency in terms of removal of material from site, as a volume reduction in the order of 10 to 1 can be expected, but careful thought needs to be given to the expense of the equipment from an installation point of view and, most important, the need to satisfy the provisions of the Clean Air Acts.

Pipeline collection systems

In terms of initial cost outlay there is a wide range of alternatives under this heading, some for individual residences and some for the common use of groups of residential units. Another key factor to appreciate is the capacity of these different systems to deal with the variable nature of the material generated. Some systems may be capable of dealing only with perishable material, and this may only represent up to 10–15 per cent of all material. In such cases, the viability of the installation has to be viewed in terms of the additional cost of extra arrangements needed to remove the remaining 85–90 per cent.

In terms of sophistication, the provision may be as simple as a sink grinder to the individual residence, or a pneumatic pipeline collection system serving several blocks of flats.

Sink grinders [25] are primarily for the dis-

or sheet steel/stainless steel, suitably profiled. Note the need to ventilate the smells that can be expected, and the facility to close off the chute while changing the collection container.

Material deposited by the resident falls under gravity to the point of collection from the point of disposal. The hopper entry point for the resident is normally located in a common part of the premises (an access corridor for example), often with free ventilation to outside air, and this helps to maintain an odour-free environment.

posal of perishable waste in the form of potato peelings, vegetable skins and the like. The grinder works
with an amount of tap water to pulverize the material in order to allow removal via an ordinary sink
waste pipe of the type referred to earlier in this
chapter. The trap provided to the waste should be
of conventional form and not a bottle type, which
would inevitably lead to blockage through pulp
accumulation (Figure 3.44).

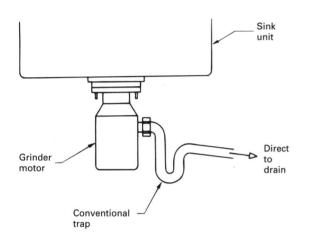

Figure 3.44 A sink grinder

As the material generated by the grinder enters
the above-ground drainage system and later the
below-ground drainage, this is known as a **water-
borne to sewer** method of disposal.

An alternative to the sink grinder, which is more
popular in other parts of Europe than the UK, is
the **Garchey system** of sink disposal. Compared
with the sink grinder, which can typically handle
10–15 per cent of all material, the Garchey method
may collect around 40–50 per cent of total refuse,
including small bottles and cans.

Instead of having a pulverizing action, the Garchey
method simply collects an amount of kitchen waste
in a bulbous receiver located directly below the sink.
A special plugged waste outlet to the sink can be
removed by the householder for the manual depositing of the material, which can include items
of up to approximately 75 mm diameter and up to
150 mm in length (Figure 3.45).

The bulbous receiver will therefore contain a

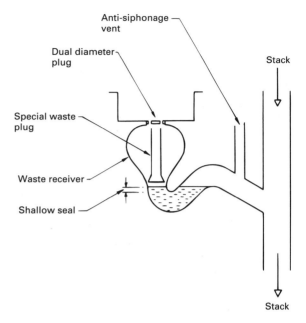

Figure 3.45 The sink receiver of the Garchey
system

mixture of water, other liquids and an amount of
solids. A larger-than-normal waste pipe (typically
150 mm diameter) will be needed to accommodate
the nature of the refuse collected, and this will
connect to a stack pipe of similar or larger diameter.

Another consequence of the nature of the material collected will be the practicality of providing
a trap seal against the entry of foul smells. As shown
in the illustration, the trap in the waste pipe is only
shallow, and this necessitates the use of an anti-
siphonage vent pipe to stabilize air pressure fluctuations and prevent induced siphonage.

When tall residential blocks are constructed the
refuse chute is really the only viable method for
the removal of refuse. Where a number of such
blocks are contemplated, refuse collection can be
beneficially influenced by the use of a **pneumatic
pipeline system**.

If the connecting pipelines are located at the foot
of each block these may be focused to one central
point of collection. This central point of collection
may have several radial pipeline arms connected
to surrounding blocks of flats and also acts as a
focus for the refuse collection vehicle, which has
only a single-stop destination. At the collection point,

on-site compaction or incineration is typically employed.

Compressed air forces the material from the base of each block of flats to the central point of collection. Clearly this is an expensive system to install, but one that can dramatically reduce costs over the life of the buildings served.

QUESTIONS

1   When assessing the likely total peak flow of discharges into an above-ground drainage system, discharge unit values are examined. On what two factors are discharge unit values based?
2   What names are applied to describe the pipework systems above ground into which all sanitary appliances discharge?
3   Why are pressure fluctuations carefully considered in the design of above-ground drainage systems, and how are they quickly neutralized?
4   In below-ground drainage installations a division is sometimes made into two forms of flow: surface water and foul water. Which discharge enters a foul drain?
5   Name six features of design in below-ground drainage systems that should ensure efficient operation.
6   In connection with below-ground drainage systems define *invert level* and *invert depth*.
7   Name four alternative methods of gaining access to a drain for the clearing of blockages.
8   Explain the difference between the operation of a septic tank and that of a cesspool.
9   How many the efficiency of refuse collection by attendant operatives be improved?
10 Why must the adoption of sink grinders for refuse disposal be considered as only part of a system for effective disposal?

REFERENCES

1   BS 6465 : Part 1 : 1984 *Code of practice for the provision, selection and installation of sanitary appliances*
2   BS 5503 : 1977 *Specification for vitreous chi-na washdown WC pans;* BS 5504 Part 4 : 1990 *Wall hung WC pans*
3   BS 4880 : Part 1 : 1973 *Stainless steel slab urinals*; BS 5520 : 1977 *Specification for vitreous china bowl urinals*
4   BS 1206 : 1974 *Specification for fireclay sinks*; BS 1244 : 1977 *Metals sinks for domestic purposes*
5   BS 1189 : 1986 *Specification for baths made from porcelain enamelled cast iron*; BS 4305 : 1989 *Specification for baths*
6   See BS 5572 : 1978 *Code of Practice for sanitary pipework*; Building Regulations 1991, Part H, clause H1, Approved Document H, Section 1, *Sanitary pipework*
7   Building Regulations 1991, Approved Document H, Tables 1 to H1, *Flow rates for sanitary appliances*
8   Building Regulations 1991, Approved Document H, Section 1, *Traps*
9   Building Regulations 1991, Approved Document H, Section 1, *Branch discharge pipes*
10 Building Regulations 1991, Approved Document H, Appendix to H1, clause A6
11 Building Regulations 1991, Approved Document H, clause H1 Section 2, *Pipe gradients and sizes*, clauses 2.10–2.14, *Bedding and backfilling*, clauses 2.16–2.18
12 Building Regulations 1991, Approved Document H, clause H1 Section 1, *Branch discharge pipes*, clause 1.11
13 BS 497 : 1976 *Specification for manhole covers, road gully gratings and frames for drainage purposes*
14 BS 1247 : 1990 *Manhole step irons*
15 Building Regulations 1991, Approved Document H, Section 2, *Clearance of blockages*, clauses 2.19–2.26
16 BS 5911 : Part 2 : 1982 *Specification for inspection chambers and gullies (precast concrete)*
17 BS 65 : 1991 *Specification for vitrified clayware pipes, fittings and joints*
18 BS 5911 : 1982 *Precast concrete pipes for drainage and sewerage*; BS 3656 : 1981 (1990) *Specification for asbestos cement pipes*; BS 437 : 1978 *Specification for cast iron spigot and socket drain pipes and fittings*; BS 4660 : 1989 *Unplasticised PVC underground drain pipes and fittings*
19 Building Regulations 1991, Clause H2, *Cess-*

pools and tanks, and Approved Document H; BS 6297 : 1983 *Code of practice for the design and installation of small sewage treatment works and cesspools*

20 Building Regulations 1991, Approved Document H, clause H2, *Capacity*, p. 14

21 Building Regulations 1991, Approved Document H, clause 1.2, *Minimum trap sizes and seal depths for appliances*

22 I.H. Seeley, *Building Technology*, Macmillan (1995)

23 BS 5906 : 1980 (1987) *Code of practice for the storage and on-site treatment of solid waste from buildings*

24 BS 1703 : 1977 *Specification for refuse chutes and hoppers*

25 BS 3456 : Part 202 : 1990 *Food waste disposal units*

4 TYPES OF HEATING SYSTEM

FUNDAMENTAL CONSIDERATIONS

The reasons for providing heating systems in buildings are threefold:

- to provide ideal thermal comfort conditions under which the occupants can live and work in a safe and efficient manner;
- to ensure that the products being used, stored or manufactured in the space are protected from the cold and damp;
- to protect the building fabric from the effects of cold weather.

The aim of this chapter is to introduce the various controllable factors relating to thermal comfort, the well-being of the occupants within the space, and the associated heating plant required to maintain the chosen design conditions.

It is not only the heating system that determines the thermal conditions in a building; many other complex factors must be considered. These include heat gains from occupants, machines, lights, processes, solar sources, moisture gains from processes, air leakage from the effects of wind, stack effect and mechanical ventilation. Another factor is the structural behaviour of light- or heavy-weight buildings, relating to thermal storage and inertia.

In designing a heating system, some of these factors may be taken into account, or may simply be considered an extra bonus.

Before dealing with the various heating systems available, it is essential to consider the factors necessary to obtain thermal comfort; the rate of heat loss from a building will then be examined.

COMFORT FACTORS [1]

The human body always attempts to keep its deep core temperature at a fixed temperature of about 37 °C. This temperature is kept by striking a balance between the heat gained and heat lost from the body. In order to achieve this balance the following factors must be considered:

- **metabolism** – the heat produced by the body due to the combination of food and oxygen within the body;
- the heat lost or gained by **convection** from or to the surface of the skin and clothing, owing to surrounding air-temperature difference;
- the heat lost or gained by **radiation** from the clothing and the skin to or from surrounding surfaces within the space;
- the heat lost by **evaporation** from the skin, and from the lungs via the respiratory tract;
- conduction (normally ignored).

The rate of heat loss by convection depends on two factors; the air temperature and the air velocity over the body. The heat gained or lost by radiation depends on the relative areas and temperatures of the surrounding surfaces. The rate of heat loss by evaporation depends on the vapour pressure of the air, and the air velocity over the body.

In order to ensure the **thermal comfort** of an occupant in a space, **six** factors have to be considered. Four are environmental variables:

- air temperature (°C);
- mean radiant temperature (°C);
- air velocity over the body (m/s);
- vapour pressure (Pa).

The remaining two are personal variables:

- activity level (MET W/m^2);
- insulation value of clothing (Clo. m^2 °C/W).

From the above, it will be seen that a person's feeling of warmth depends not only on the air temperature, but also on the relationship between this and the other five factors.

An understanding of how the human body responds to these six factors is essential when considering heating or cooling systems for buildings.

Typical internal design conditions are given in the CIBSE Guide A1 [2]. Once the internal design temperatures have been selected, the CIBSE Guide A2 [3] is consulted to obtain the external temperatures for any given area. With these two temperatures, the rate of heat loss or gain by the methods given in the CIBSE Guide A9 [4] or McMullan [5] can be determined.

It is essential that certain minimum temperatures are achieved to meet the requirements of legislation covering offices and factories. Additionally, in the UK a maximum air temperature of 19 °C is stipulated by legislation for building energy conservation.

Having determined the rate of heat loss from the space, heat emitters and heat generators (boilers) have to be selected, in order to meet the design conditions.

HEATING SYSTEMS [6]

Heating systems can be divided into local heating and central heating.

Local heating can be considered as consisting of any of the following categories:

- electric fires, which can be further subdivided into: radiant heaters and convectors, either natural or forced (These may use either peak period or off-peak electricity. The reasons for off peak, and the methods used, are discussed later.);
- solid fuel, open or closed fire;
- gas fire, either radiant or convective;
- oil stove.

These appliances are used in houses and small commercial establishments, and are called **local heaters**, as the heat is from a local source in the room (not from a central source, as in a central heating system).

Central heating systems can be divided into the following related subsystems:

- the utilization subsystem;
- the distribution subsystem;
- the energy conversion subsystem;
- the control subsystem.

The **utilization subsystem** [7] is the final part of the heating system required to produce the heating effect in the space. The type of heat emitter selected depends on the type of heat transfer fluid used. These fluids are covered under distribution and energy conversion subsystems.

The first type of heat emitter that comes to mind when considering a heating system is the **radiator**. The name 'radiator' is a misnomer, as by far the greatest proportion of the heat emitted is by convection.

The principal types of heat emitter can be subdivided into:

- natural convectors (including radiators);
- forced convectors;
- heated floors ceilings and walls.

Distribution system [8] may be classed as low-temperature hot water, medium-temperature hot water, high-temperature hot water, steam systems or air systems. In some cases the term 'low pressure' may be used instead of the word 'temperature'. Wet systems use pipework; ductwork is used in air systems.

The **energy conversion subsystem** [9] relates to the source of energy provided: primary energy relates to fossil fuels, while secondary energy relates to electricity. These energy sources must be related to the methods of firing, and the heat-generating equipment. In the energy conversion subsystem, it is essential to consider whether pollution of the atmosphere, water and land results from the conversion process.

Heating systems require some form of automatic control of the heat emitters, distribution flow rates, and the fuel and energy usage in the energy conversion process taking place in the heat generating equipment. The purpose of the **control subsystem** [10] is to ensure that the system operates within safe limits of temperature and pressure, to control the space temperature to the required design conditions, and (most important) to ensure that the system operates with maximum energy efficiency.

Figure 4.1 summarizes the flow paths that have been described. After this brief introduction to the subject, it is now essential to enlarge on each of the subsystems, starting with the utilization subsystem (heat emitters).

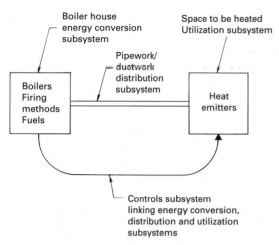

Figure 4.1   Related heating subsystems

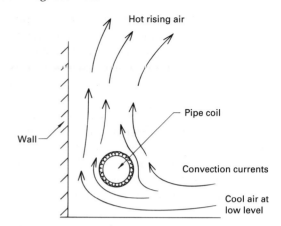

Figure 4.2   Pipework as a heat emitter

UTILIZATION SUBSYSTEM

A heat emitter has to provide a heat output to the space where it is positioned. The heat that it produces must be adequate to maintain the space at the internal design condition at an appropriate outside winter air temperature. The output of the emitters matches the sum of the fabric and ventilation heat losses in the space: the greater the temperature difference between the surface of the heat emitter and the room air, and the surrounding surfaces, the greater the required heat output.

The simplest form of heat emitter is a pipe conveying hot water. This method of heating spaces 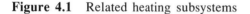 was common for many years; however, it has the disadvantage of requiring large-diameter pipes to provide the heating surface. It can be used below skylights to counteract downdraughts, below lockers in the changing rooms of sports halls, or below the benches in glasshouses to aid plant propagation.

The greatest percentage of the heat transfer from pipes at low temperature is by convection; radiation is only secondary. Figure 4.2 shows the convection currents set up around pipework. When one pipe is stacked above another, the heat output is not in fact doubled, as the radiation and convective heat transfer are reduced.

Radiators

The most common type of heat emitter used for domestic and commercial heating is the family of the so-called **radiators**. In these, the percentage of heat emission by radiation at low temperature is less than 30 per cent, and in some cases only 10 per cent; hence convection is predominant. The correct term to use should be **natural convector**; however, over the years the name 'radiator' has been used, so we follow this convention in this book. The output of this type of appliance does not usually exceed 6 kW.

The type most commonly used in the UK today is the pressed steel **panel radiator**, with either single or double panels. These sections may or may not be fitted with fins; the fin type has a greater heat output than a plain panel section. A twin-panel radiator has a greater heat transfer surface area than a single panel of the same length and height. Inspection of manufacturer's data will, however, show that the output is not double that of a single panel, as the radiant component is not doubled.

The correct heat output from radiators is achieved by selecting various heights or lengths from the manufacturer's data. The surface temperature of such radiators averages 75 °C, which is too high for certain buildings, such as an old person's home. Special radiators are used in such areas to reduce the risk of skin contact burns; these have surface temperatures of less than 43 °C. Care must be taken with pressed steel radiators, as they are prone to corrosion; water treatment is therefore recommended.

Figure 4.3 shows a typical pressed steel radiator.

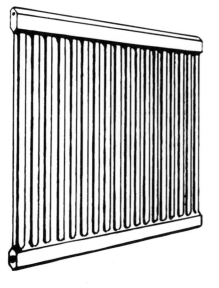

Figure 4.3   Pressed steel single-panel radiator

The **column radiator** is constructed from cast iron, and was the only type available before the 1950s. Figure 4.4 gives some idea of its shape. Its advantage over the pressed steel radiator is that it has a better resistance to corrosion. Owing to a left- and right-hand thread arrangement, the unit can be extended by using a barrel nipple.

The disadvantages of cast iron are that it is very heavy, and the projection from the wall is greater than that of a pressed steel radiator. Cast aluminium alloy radiators are finding a larger market because of their lower weight.

It is normal to mount radiators on the external wall under the window sill, as in this position the rising convection currents reduce the discomfort caused by cold draughts emanating from the window.

A radiator shelf located too close to the top of the radiator will reduce its output, as will a cupboard. If a cover of this type is intended, it is necessary to install a radiator with a greater output. It is essential to ensure that all radiators are adequately supported to the wall, as considerable damage can be caused if one pulls away from the wall.

It is essential to provide a free air inlet at low level and outlet at high level so as to allow convection currents.

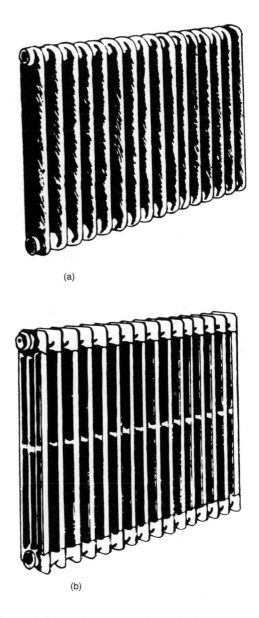

(a)

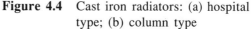

(b)

Figure 4.4   Cast iron radiators: (a) hospital type; (b) column type

Radiators are unable to withstand high pressures, and are only to be used on low-pressure hot water (low temperature).

Convectors

Convectors are subdivided into two groups, **natural** and **forced**. Heat transfer in both these cases is mainly by convection, some 10–15 per cent more than that produced by a (so-called) radiator. The radiant component has to be considered for a radiator, while for a convector it can be ignored.

Natural convectors consist of a metal case containing a finned pipe coil. The fins increase the surface area of the pipe and the heat transfer from the pipe to the room air.

The term 'natural' is used because these convectors rely on thermal forces to produce the heat exchange. Basically, cool dense air at low level enters the unit at the base; it comes into contact with the coils and is heated up, thus becoming less dense; it then rises. The taller the case, the greater the thermal force (stack effect), which increases the heat output of the unit. Control of the output is achieved by means of the damper.

The output for a given length is greater than that from a radiator, owing to its projection from the wall; however, it does take up more floor space from the wall. A typical arrangement is shown in Figure 4.5.

The **forced convector** depends on a fan, or fans, to pass the low-level cool air over the heater battery. The fan motor may be three-speed: slow, medium and high. As the speed is increased the velocity of the air over the finned tube is increased, producing a greater heat output. The units have filters at the air inlet, and can be controlled by means of a room thermostat. The units may cause complaints of noise when on high speed, and when the bearings are damaged. Figure 4.6 shows the internal arrangement of such units.

Other forced convectors that may be used are **unit heaters** (Figure 4.7). These are mainly found in industrial heating applications. They are mounted

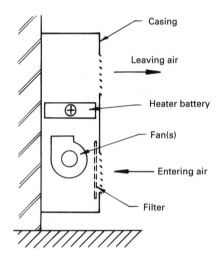

Figure 4.6   Fan convector

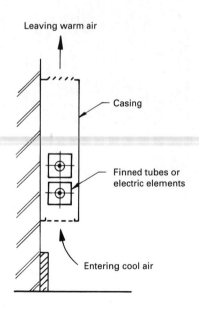

Figure 4.5   Natural convector

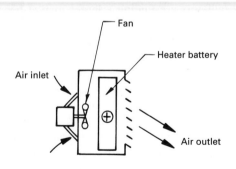

Figure 4.7   Unit heater

at high level, where they blow the air horizontally near the walls, or vertically down into the centre of the space. Free-standing floor models may also be used; some are directly fired by either oil or gas. Care has to be taken to ensure that the leaving air temperature (LAT) and the leaving air velocity (LAV) are not too high in the occupied zone, otherwise discomfort will be experienced. Electrical block storage heaters with fans, using off-peak electricity are also forced convectors.

Radiant panels

In industrial applications higher fluid temperatures are employed to supply radiant panels. Such panels are mounted at high level to avoid contact burns.

This type of heater may simply consist of a steel pipe welded to a steel plate (Figure 4.8), or a continuous radiant strip, in which case consideration of the rate of thermal expansion is essential. These heat emitters depend on low-temperature hot water, medium-temperature hot water, high-temperature hot water, or steam supplied in pipes from the boiler house. If the boiler house is some distance away, heat is lost from the pipework before it reaches the space to be heated. This heat loss represents a lowering of the efficiency of the system.

This problem is overcome by using a direct heating system, as shown in Figure 4.9. Gas is supplied direct to the high-level duct, one end having

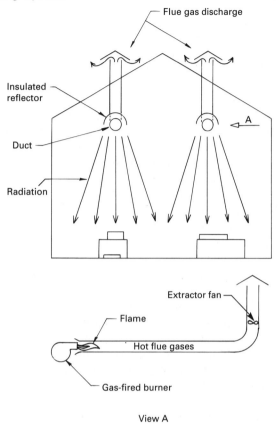

Figure 4.9 Direct-fired radiant heating

a gas burner, and the other an extractor fan, which draws the products of combustion to be discharged to a safe location outside the building. The gas flame and the products of combustion heat the walls of the duct; this heat is radiated down to the occupied zone by means of the reflector plate. Surfaces in the radiant path are heated, producing radiation and convection components. With this type of system, the temperature gradient between the floor and ceiling/roof is much less than that if a warm-air system is used.

Floor-warming system

Another form of radiant heating system is the floor- or ceiling-warming system. Floor-warming systems were introduced into England by the Romans in 55 BC. They were called hypocausts, and were

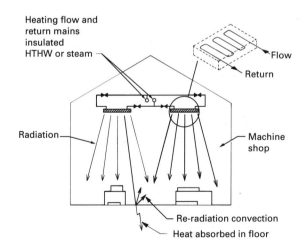

Figure 4.8 Radiant heating panels

simply a suspended floor that had a fire and allowed the flue gases to pass beneath it.

Modern systems consist of either pipe coils or electrical resistance cables embedded in the floor. The pipe coils are of 15 or 20 mm diameter and may be copper, mild steel or plastics buried at a depth of about 50 mm below the floor finish at spacings to suit the heat loading. The plastics pipes are now the most popular, as the operating temperatures are low, and corrosion will not occur. The floor slab is insulated on both the edges and perimeters to reduce downward heat loss. Good thermal comfort conditions are produced, and the resulting temperature gradient is small.

The flow temperature in the pipework has to be kept low and controlled, not only to stop excessive expansion of the floor slab, but also to keep the floor surface temperature at about 25 °C, otherwise foot discomfort will be experienced.

If the return water temperature entering the heat generator is too low, severe thermal stresses will be set up in the boiler shell, and in the case of oil- or coal-burning heat generators the sulphur in the fuel will on combustion turn into sulphur dioxide. Under boiler operating conditions, if dew-point is reached, this SO_2 will turn to sulphuric acid (H_2SO_4), causing corrosion of the boiler shell. To prevent this from occurring a heat exchanger is fed from the primary flow and return, with a mixing valve on the secondary circuit, thus ensuring that the correct floor coil temperature is maintained.

Electric resistance cables buried in the floor concrete operate on an off-peak supply. Heat is stored in the floor slab during the off-peak period. The amount stored must be capable of providing enough heat to meet the design heat loss during the peak period. One of the problems of the electric floor warming system is the difficulty of controlling the heat. Unlike a radiator system, which can be turned off if the space becomes too warm, the floor-warming system cannot be turned off, and the heat stored in the slab will continue to be liberated when it is not required. This feature has in some instances worked against its popularity. Figure 4.10 shows a section of a floor panel system.

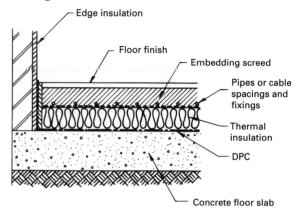

Figure 4.10   Basic layout of a ground-floor slab with a floor-warming system

ENERGY CONVERSION SUBSYSTEM

A brief introduction to the study of fuels, their advantages and disadvantages, methods of burning and the types of heat generator used, is essential to the understanding of building services energy systems.

A building's heat requirements are provided by a heat generator, which obtains its heat from fossil fuels, alternative energy sources or electricity.

The solid, liquid or gaseous fuels burnt must convert the heat trapped in them efficiently, into low-, medium-, high-temperature (-pressure) hot water, steam or air. This heat is passed to the distribution subsystem and then to the utilization subsystem (heat exchangers/emitters). The heat generation takes place in a device commonly called the **boiler**. Strictly speaking, a boiler is a device in which the water is allowed to boil, but this only actually occurs in a steam system. Any other device in which water is heated, but no steam is produced, ought to be called a heat generator.

The heat transfer from the fuel to the water, regardless of the type of heat generator, takes place as shown in Figure 4.11. This heat transfer is a combination of radiation and convection from the flame, conduction through the walls and then convection from the wall to the heat transfer medium. If soot is allowed to build up on the fire side, or lime or scale on the water side, the thermal efficiency of the process will drop, owing to the in-

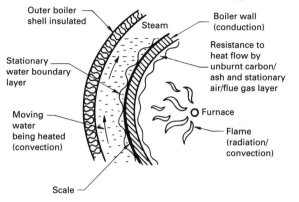

Figure 4.11 Boiler heat transfer

crease in thermal resistance. It is therefore essential to keep these surfaces clean in order to achieve the maximum efficiency.

Many types of heat generator/boiler are used in building service applications. These are now described.

Cast iron boilers [11] are manufactured from grey cast iron in standard sections, and are popular in smaller-sized installations. Any fuel can be burnt to produce low-temperature/pressure hot water. They have the advantage that the output may be increased simply by adding extra sections. This arrangement allows them to be built up in areas where access is limited. The sections are held together by tie bars and barrel nipples.

The design and efficiency of this type of unit have improved over the past 40 years. However, they cannot be used in tall buildings, as the static pressure is too great for the strength of the material; the same applies to steel and cast iron radiators.

A typical cast iron sectional boiler is shown in Figure 4.12.

Package shell boilers [12] are more expensive than cast iron; they are used for both water and

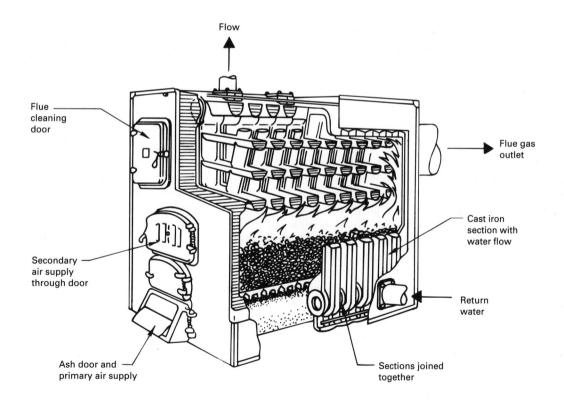

Figure 4.12 Cast iron sectional boiler with hand-fired bed (*Note*: Very few hand-fired boilers are found in use today)

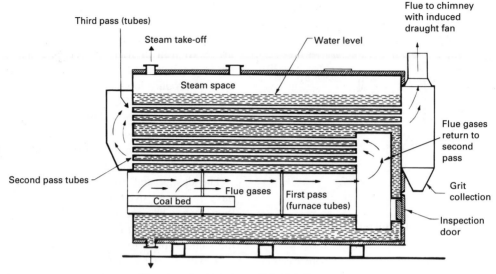

Figure 4.13 Coal-fired package three-pass shell boiler

steam, and are capable of withstanding greater pressures than cast iron. They are supplied pressure-tested, complete with all fittings and thermal insulation (see Figure 4.13).

The combustion products reverse upon themselves in the flueways, thus ensuring that as much heat as possible is extracted from the flue gases.

If this type of boiler is used for hot water at various pressures, it is known as a **flooded system**, and it is essential that its operating pressure is below the saturation temperature (boiling point) of water. The actual temperature difference below the boiling point is known as the **anti-flash margin**. In a steam boiler, a space (steam space) is allowed above the water line, resulting in a large shell.

The unit design depends on the fuel being burnt, and a solid fuel unit may be up to 60 per cent larger than an equivalent-duty oil- or gas-fired unit. This type of boiler is known as a **fire tube**, as the products of combustion pass within the multiple tubes of the gas passage-ways.

The **water tube boiler** [13] is used for power generation, with operating temperatures in the 60 °C range. As the name suggests, water flows through tubes, which are heated by radiation and convection from the combustion process.

The operation of the **electrode boiler** [14] must not be considered as being similar to the conventional resistive element water heater, such as a kettle or immersion heater. An electrode boiler uses a three-phase 415 V or greater electricity supply. Electrical current is allowed to pass between suspended electrodes, converting the electricity directly into heat (Figure 4.14).

If the electrode boiler is used as a steam boiler, its output is controlled by increasing or decreasing

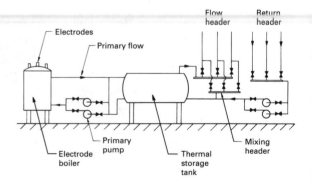

Figure 4.14 Electrode boiler

the area of the electrode in the water, whereas in a water boiler the electrodes must be fully flooded to prevent steam formation. The control is achieved by a ceramic shield, which can be raised or lowered to vary the current flowing through the water.

Electrode boilers normally operate from an off-peak supply, and hence they require a large volume storage vessel to hold the heat content to meet the daily demands.

Conventional gas-fired boilers have a thermal efficiency of about 80 per cent, and operate at a high flue gas temperature to ensure that condensation of the flue gases does not cause boiler corrosion. The **condensing boiler**, on the other hand, is designed to promote condensation of the moisture in the flue gases and, by so doing, recover the latent and sensible heat that would normally be lost as waste heat in the stack.

Condensing boilers can use either natural gas or LPG, and are capable of thermal efficiencies above 90 per cent, thus saving fuel and reducing the greenhouse CO_2 emission.

The condensing boiler differs from the conventional boiler in that the flue gases pass through a larger heat exchanger in order to remove the maximum amount of heat from the gases. The latent heat extraction produces condensation, so a drain connection is required to discharge into a drain.

FUELS [15]

The fossil fuels – coal, oil and gas – provide more than 90 per cent of the world's energy demand. As these fuels are finite, with diminishing reserves, scarcity will result in price increases. Hence the need to develop alternative sources, to meet the energy gap, which for oil and gas will occur in the 21st century. Modern boiler plant is capable of utilizing an extremely wide range of fuels, which can be classified into:

- solid;
- liquid;
- gaseous.

Solid

The main solid fuels are listed in Table 4.1. Refuse-derived fuels (rdf) are also solid; they vary in calorific value, but in general they are at least 50 per cent of bituminous fuel.

Table 4.1 *Solid fuels*

Nature	Carbon (% weight)	Calorific value (MJ/kg)
Wood	50	14.6
Peat	57.5	15.9
Coals		
Lignite	70	21.6
Bitumious	77–88	25.8–34.8
Semi-bituminous	90.5	34.8
Semi-anthracite	93	34.2
Anthracite	94	34.6

Coals are classified by rank, which is related to their age and depth of burial. **Low-rank** coals include lignites and brown coals, and represent an early stage of coal formation. **Medium rank** includes a wide range of bituminous coals. The highest rank are the **anthracites**. Having a high carbon content, they are hard and difficult to burn. The pollutant levels produced are less than those of the lower-rank coals, which have a high volatile content.

Table 4.1 lists only the carbon content of coals. Various other elements are found in coal in varying degrees: hydrogen, oxygen, nitrogen, sulphur and ash.

Peat is about 1 million years old, while bituminous coals are about 250 million years old.

Liquid fuel (petroleum)

In 1859, oil was struck at a depth of 21 m by Captain Edwin Drake at Titusville, Pennsylvania. This started the oil industry as we know it today. Nowadays, oil is collected from depths in excess of 6000 m.

Unlike coal, which can be traced to organic remains in swamps, the origin of crude oil and natural gas is still the subject of debate. However, it is assumed to be formed from aquatic animal and

Table 4.2   *Classification of fuel oils*

	Class	Net calorific value (MJ/kg)
Kerosene	C2	43.6
Gas oil	D	42.7
Light fuel oil	E	41.0
Medium fuel oil	F	40.5
Heavy fuel oil	G	40.0

plant life deposited with inorganic matter, such as sediments in tropical seas.

Fuel oils are classified as shown in Table 4.2.

The basic principle of oil refining is to separate the crude oil into its major chemical components by heating and distilling off the fractions in a tower. The distillation fractions of the lowest boiling point are separated as petroleum, ether, methane, and ethane (gasoline), then propane, butane, kerosene, gas oils, lubricating oils, then heavy fuel oil, followed by asphalt and tar.

Typical distillation of crude oil will give 20–30 per cent gasoline, 30–45 per cent intermediate oils, and 25–50 per cent residual oils. To obtain more gasoline, a cracking process is used. This requires further heating or a catalyst process, giving a by-product of petroleum coke. Fuel oils are hydrocarbons, this describing the hydrogen and carbon in them. Sulphur is also present in varying amounts.

Gaseous fuels

Liquefied petroleum gas (LPG), consisting of butane and propane, is derived from the petrochemical process. It is used for process work, and in areas where natural gas is not available.

Natural gas consists of about 93 per cent methane, having a calorific value of 38.7 MJ/m^3, which is twice as great as the calorific value of town gas (coal gas), which contains the poisonous gas carbon monoxide, and was used before the introduction of North Sea gas. Methane as a gas, may be obtained from landfill sites, coal mines or sewage treatment works.

The selection of the fuel type is always a problem. Many factors have to be considered, including the availability and certainty of delivery; pollution aspects; the cost of supply, initial cost and maintenance; the area required for storage; and the political implications of using a certain fuel. Each fuel has to be considered on its merits.

FIRING METHODS

To release the energy trapped in a fuel, combustion is necessary, and an exothermic chemical reaction takes place between fuel and oxygen, resulting in heat liberation. Combustion will not commence or continue below the fuel's **ignition temperature**, or without sufficient air being provided to the fuel in a turbulent manner. Air contains 79 per cent nitrogen and 21 per cent oxygen. The oxygen is required for combustion, but the nitrogen takes no part in the process, apart from serving to cool the flame.

Fuels contain varying amounts of carbon, hydrogen and sulphur, all of which provide heat when supplied with the correct amount of oxygen. Carbon, if supplied with the correct amount of air, releases heat and produces carbon dioxide (CO_2). If inadequate air is supplied heat is lost, and carbon monoxide (CO) results as well as carbon dioxide. Any sulphur in the fuel will burn to sulphur dioxide, while hydrogen burns to water vapour, both of these processes producing heat.

Not all the chemical energy contained in the fuel is released as heat energy into the heating system, as combustion is never 100 per cent efficient. Some heat is lost by radiation, conduction, convection, unburnt carbon, and in the flue gases.

Different combustion techniques are required to burn solid, liquid or gaseous fuels.

Solid fuel burning

Coal may be burnt on a static grate, such as a domestic fire. As the efficiency of this process is low, mechanical grates are used for all commercial and industrial applications, because they operate at higher efficiencies.

Primary air is supplied beneath the grate, and is forced through the fuel bed by means of a fan. With ignition the oxygen in the air combines with the carbon in the coal, producing CO_2 and CO. These gases rise with the volatile vapours from the bed, where they are mixed with the secondary air, to complete the combustion process. The term **primary air** relates to air passing through the fuel bed, while **secondary air** is that entering above the combustion zone. The physical size of the coal dictates how much combustion air has to be provided.

Many types of mechanical stoker are used: the principal types are the sprinkler, the coking, the underfeed and the chain grate. We will discuss the underfeed and the chain grate stokers.

The **underfeed stoker** [16] is used on small installations. The fuel is fed by a conveyer screw from a hopper to the retort, which is a cast iron and firebrick pot. As the fuel passes up through the retort pot, high-pressure air is fed through jets (tuyeres) near the top of the retort. It is at this level that combustion takes place.

The volatile matter produced from the freshly entering coal has to pass through the incandescent bed, ensuring that the correct ignition temperature is reached to give smoke-free operation.

Figure 4.15 shows the arrangement of this method of firing.

The **chain grate stoker** is used for much larger installations (Figure 4.16).

The hopper feeds fuel via a guillotine door onto an endless chain. The height of the guillotine is set to vary the height of the fuel bed. The chain carries the fuel under an ignition arch, causing the fuel to burn. The ash and clinker produced are discharged at the back of the conveyer into the ash pit; ash removal and storage is required.

With solid fuel, care has to be taken in selecting the correct rank of coal; failure to do this will result in poor combustion.

Liquid fuel burning [17]

Liquid fuel has to be atomized in order to reach a point where ignition takes place. Ignition may be by a gas flame or by an electric arc.

As with solid fuel firing, many different types of burner are used. The simplest type is a vaporizing

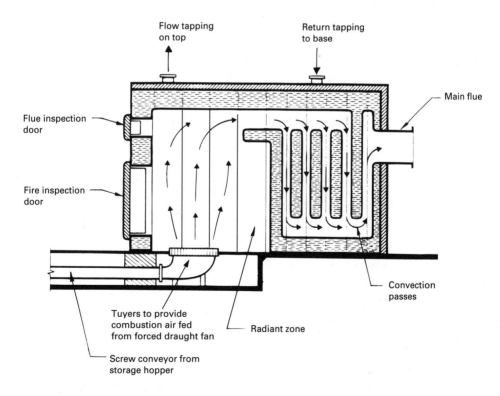

Figure 4.15 Cast iron sectional boiler with underfeed stoker

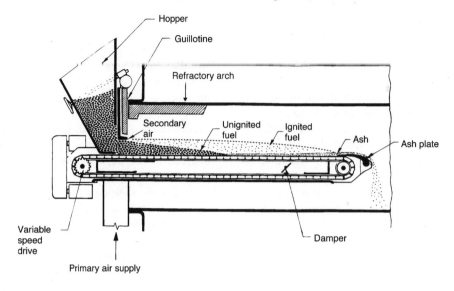

Figure 4.16   Section of chain grate stoker

burner, such as is found in paraffin heaters. The burner used in commercial and industrial systems include pressure jet atomizers, spinning-cup atomizers, spill jet, steam or air-assisted, high-, medium- and low-pressure blast burners.

The operation of the **pressure jet burner** is as follows. Oil is fed from the storage tank to the burner, and on passing through a pump is pressurized and forced through a nozzle with tangential slots. These slots are designed to give spin to the oil before discharge into the boiler. A hollow conical spray is formed on leaving the jet; this is broken down by the introduction of the combustion air into the spray. Ignition of this spray is achieved by a high-voltage electrical spark from the tips of electrodes.

Most oils have to be heated in order for them to flow in the pipeline and to ensure that the atomization produces a droplet size that will ensure complete combustion in the boiler. The atomization pressure is critical; depending on the burner type it will range from 680 kPa to 1.7 MPa (6.8–17 bar).

Figure 4.17 shows a typical oil-heating system layout from the storage tank to the burner.

Gas burners [18]

A gas has to be mixed with combustion air in the correct proportions in order for it to burn. This mixing process is not as difficult as that necessary for the burning of oil. As with the other fuels, many different burner types are used, ranging from the standard domestic and small commercial type (known as the **atmospheric burner**) to the high-pressure and dual-fuel burners used in larger installations.

The atmospheric burner induces its own air, while other low-pressure burners require a fan for the supply of combustion air and operate over a pressure range of 250 Pa to 1 kPa (2.5–10 mbar) gas pressure. A high-pressure burner operates over a range from 12 to 175 mbar. Figure 4.18 shows the arrangement of an atmospheric injection burner.

For further coverage of gas systems see Chapter 7.

Flue systems

All fossil-fuel-burning appliances require a flue, the requirements depending on the fuel being burnt.

For a solid or liquid fuel, the purpose of the flue is twofold:

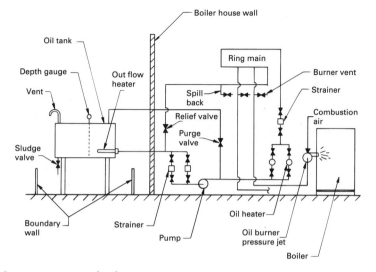

Figure 4.17   Oil supply to a pressure jet burner

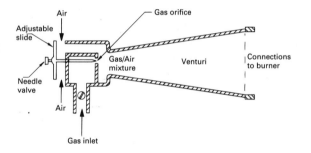

Figure 4.18   Atmospheric injector burner

- to create a draught through the boiler, to ensure good mixing of the volatiles in the fuel
  with the combustion air in order to ensure the
  maximum combustion efficiency;
- to ensure that the products of combustion are
  removed from the combustion zone and discharged outside the building, where the corrosive and toxic products will not cause any
  problems.

When a gaseous fuel is burnt, the entering gas pressure provides the draught, and the purpose of the
flue is only to remove the products of combustion.

The draught may be created either by natural
means, relying on the cooler combustion air displacing the hot flue gases, or by mechanical means,
requiring a fan or fans. In the latter case the draught
may be forced or induced or balanced.

Chimneys have to be designed so that they can:

- handle the volume of flue gases produced by
  the boilers;
- ensure that condensation does not occur in the
  flue;
- withstand the wind pressures imposed on them;
- reduce friction of the flue gases to a minimum;
- ensure that the combustion products are removed
  away from adjacent areas (the Clean Air Act
  and the Chimney Memorandum) 1956 and 1968
  stipulate the height of stack required for a particular area);
- ensure that down draughts do not cause spill
  out from the boilers (in this case care has to be
  taken in making sure that the chimney outlet is
  higher than adjacent buildings);
- provide cleaning doors.

Flues for gas boilers are covered in Chapter 7.

DISTRIBUTION SUBSYSTEM

Once the water or air has been heated it has to be distributed in pipework or ductwork to the point of use.

Most domestic and small commercial applications use **low-temperature hot water systems**. The flow temperature ranges from 40 to 100 °C. For larger installations medium-temperature hot water is used, its operating range being from 100 to 120 °C. If greater operating temperatures are required, the system is classed as a **high-temperature hot water system**, operating at temperatures in excess of 120 °C. A steam system is also listed as high temperature; however, low-temperature operation is possible, by the use of a vacuum to lower the boiling point.

Distribution systems are classified according to:

- mode of water circulation;
- water temperatures as given above;
- the layout of pipework connecting the heat generators to the heat emitters.

Mode of circulation

Water may flow in a pipe network by either thermosiphonic flow (gravity forces) or by forced flow (pumped or accelerated).

In the early days of central heating the **gravity system** was the only method. Its operation depends on hot water at, say, 80 °C flow rising up the pipe leaving the boiler. On reaching the heating units a temperature drop of 20 °C is allowed: hence the leaving water temperature is 60 °C. Water at 80 °C has a density of 971.8 kg/m³, whereas the water returning to the heat generator, being cooler, is more dense, having a density of 977.7 kg/m³. It is the 5.9 kg/m³ difference between the flow and return that causes circulation to take place.

The disadvantages of such a system are that the circulation is very sluggish, and that large-diameter pipes are required to reduce friction. For these reasons the system has been replaced by the **accelerated system**, which requires a pump (circulator). This arrangement helps to overcome the resistance of the pipework, resulting in smaller pipework and a quicker response in the heating of the space. The

temperature drop (difference) between flow and return in this instance is usually about 10 °C, having a flow of 80°C and a return of about 70 °C.

Operating temperature

The operating temperature selected depends on the application; commercial/industrial heating may operate at a higher temperature than domestic heating. Floor-warming systems require lower temperatures than a radiator system.

System layout

Systems can be either **open** or **closed**. The open system has a feed and expansion tank open to the atmosphere, which means that the water temperature must be kept well below boiling point in order to stop steam from being formed. The closed low-temperature system can reach 100 °C, as water expansion takes place in a sealed pressure vessel.

Both the open and closed systems can have their distribution pipework arranged in a number of different ways. **One-pipe systems** (Figure 4.19) include:

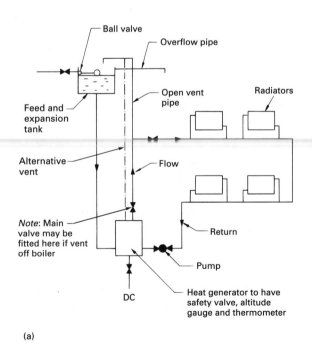

(a)

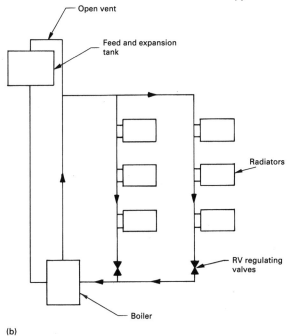

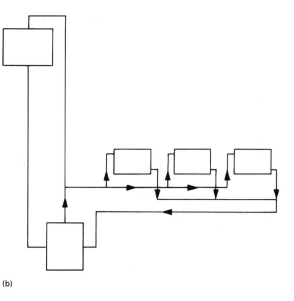

(b)

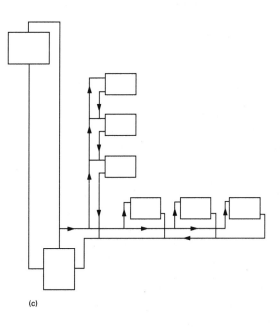

(c)

Figure 4.19 Typical one-pipe heating systems: (a) (opposite, below) one-pipe ring main; (b) one-pipe drop

- one-pipe ring main;
- one-pipe drop.

Two-pipe systems (Figure 4.20) include:

- two-pipe with direct return;
- two-pipe with reversed return;
- two-pipe rising;
- two-pipe drop.

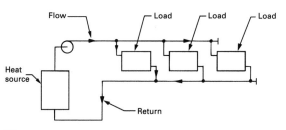

(a)

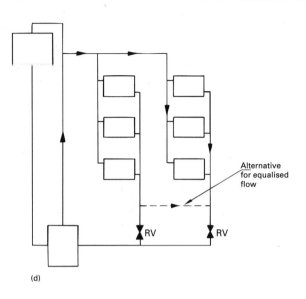

(d)

Figure 4.20 Typical two-pipe heating systems: (page 57) (a) two-pipe with direct return; (b) two-pipe with reversed return (equalized flow); (c) two-pipe rising (upfeed); and (above) (d) two-pipe drop

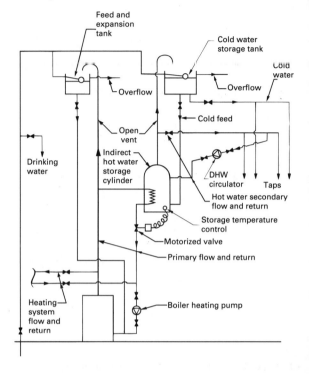

Figure 4.21 Typical low-temperature hot water and DHW system

Basic elements of a low-temperature (-pressure) hot water heating system (LTHW)

The general arrangement of an LPHW system is shown in Figure 4.21.

(1)   The mains water enters through the ball valve in the feed and expansion tank (F & E tank). the word 'expansion' is used because when the system is filled cold, say at 10 °C, the water has a certain volume. On heating the water, its volume increases. When heated to 80 °C, the water expands by about 4 per cent of its own volume: hence the tank must be capable of holding this rate of expansion without the water discharging through the overflow.

(2)   In the gravity system the heat generator increases the flow temperature, causing the water to rise up the flow pipe from the boiler. On cooling, its density increases, producing

circulation in the pipework. In the accelerated system, a pump is used to create the circulation, and the gravity forces are insignificant. The accelerated system uses smaller pipes, and as the circulation is faster, the heat-up time of the system is less than that of the gravity system.

(3)   Heat is liberated in the pipework leading to the space to be heated, as well as in the heat emitter in the room. This heat loss represents a temperature change, and the cooler return water returns to the heat generator for further heating.

The purpose of the open vent pipe is to allow the water to expand without a pressure build-up taking place in the system.

The down cold feed, as well as acting as the system fill, also provides for the expansion of hot water or the contraction of cold water. The LTHW system may be closed by using a **pressure vessel**. This is a sphere with a dividing membrane at its diameter; above the diaphragm is a gas cushion. When cold, the water below this occupies a given volume; on heating, it expands against the diaphragm, causing the gas pressure to build up. This increase in pressure allows the water to be heated up to temperatures of, say, 100 °C without the formation of steam.

In domestic and small commercial installations, it is normal to use copper pipe; in larger systems steel pipe is used. The term **small bore** is often used, as this name was introduced in the early days when the gravity system was being replaced by the accelerated systems. During the 1960s another term, **micro-bore** or **minibore**, was introduced. This refers to circuits using tubes less than 15 mm diameter; various sizes are available (6, 8, 10 or 12 mm). these micro-bore tubes are connected to a manifold, with one circuit for each radiator. A typical layout is shown in Figure 4.22.

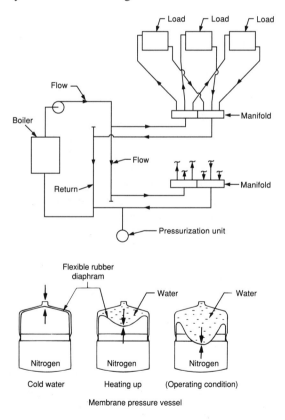

Figure 4.22 Micro-bore system with sealed expansion tank

Systems other than LTHW

When temperatures higher than 80 °C are required for process, factory or district heating, the system is pressurized by one of the following methods:

- by imposing a head of water on the system: the greater the head (pressure), the higher the operating temperature (this arrangement requires the use of a water tank at high level);
- if a steam boiler is available, by applying steam pressure to the water surface;
- by making use of the pressure generated by expanding water against a diaphragm, with nitrogen on one side and the expanding water on the other side;
- by gas using a spill tank which provides a storage space for the expanding water.

Regardless of the type of system, the pipe sizes must be designed so that they are capable of conveying the correct quantity of fluid (kg/s), to ensure that the heating units are capable of meeting the design requirements.

Figure 4.23 shows a typical layout of a high-temperature hot water system. A system of this type is used for heating large developments. It has the advantage that it uses smaller-diameter pipes than those required for the same load in a LTHW system. The disadvantages are that the plant is expensive, and skilled labour is required in its installation.

Steam systems

Steam is used for the space heating of industrial areas, as well as providing heat for process requirements.

A system that uses water as the heating medium uses only the **sensible heat** in the water. Sensible heat is the heat contained in the fluid, as opposed to **latent heat**, which is the heat contained in steam. A steam system makes full use of the latent heat in the steam. If steam at a temperature of 140 °C is allowed to condense, changing from steam to water, 2144.7 kJ is liberated for every kg. The remaining water has only 589.2 kJ/kg contained in it.

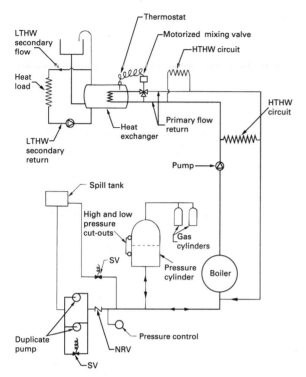

Figure 4.23   High-temperature hot water system

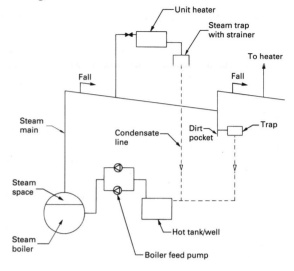

Figure 4.24   Steam heating system

CONTROL SUBSYSTEM

During the generation, distribution and use of heat, it is essential to ensure that the heat is used efficiently. This is achieved by the use of measuring instruments, and temperature and pressure controls.

The theory relating to controls is highly mathematical and complex, and lies outside the scope of this book. We shall examine only some simple control applications. The control system may operate on thermal expansion, pneumatic, or electrically controlled systems.

The whole aim of any control system is to ensure that various set design conditions, relating to temperature, moisture content, pressure or flow rates, are maintained. The components of a control system are:

* sensing element;
* controller;
* actuator.

The **sensing element** measures the value of the controlled variable, such as temperature, (thermostat) pressure, moisture content and flow.

The **controllers** receive inputs from the sensors. These inputs are related to design conditions or set

When using steam for heating it is essential that all the heat is removed from the steam. This is achieved by the use of a **steam trap**, which is a device that will only allow the low-grade hot water to leave the trap. The pipework layout of a steam system is different from that of other water systems; it is arranged in a sawtooth manner, to allow condensate collection as shown in Figure 4.24.

The maintenance costs of steam systems are high, owing to the constant attention required for traps, water treatment and corrosion problems.

The systems covered up to now, apart from the direct gas-fired radiant heating system and convectors, are classed as **wet systems**. A dry system is a warm air heating system, taking the form of the systems covered in Chapter 5. The main difference is being that heating only is provided, and not hot water.

points, and generate output signals to operate a control device.

The **actuator** converts the electrical or pneumatic energy into either rotary or linear motion. This conversion process creates a change in the controlled variable, by operating valves or dampers. The subject is complex, but the diagrams in Figure 4.25 will give an understanding of the basic operations involved.

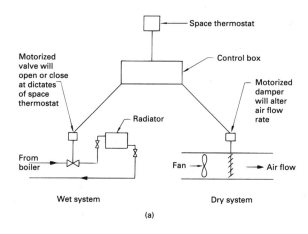

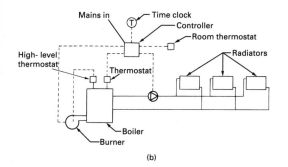

Figure 4.25 Basic temperature control: (a) wet and dry systems; (b) LTHW gas/oil-fired boiler

SOLAR HEATING

Use can be made of the solar gain on a panel, as shown in Figure 4.26, or the heat gain on a passive wall for the heating of buildings (Figure 4.27).

A **plate collector** is a panel with pipe coils bonded to it. The collector is inclined at an angle in order

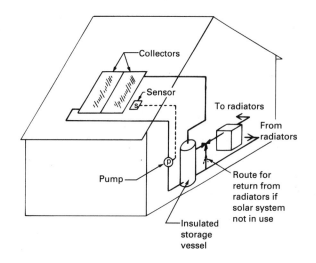

Figure 4.26 Solar heating

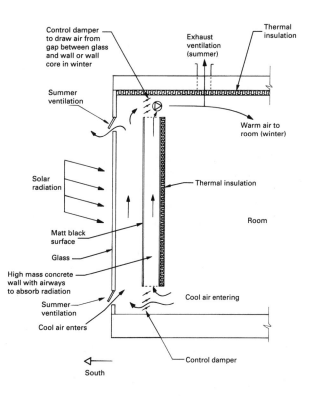

Figure 4.27 Trombe wall solar heating

to receive the maximum intensity of solar radiation at a given time of the year. The heated water from the panel is transferred to a well-insulated storage vessel, where it is used for either domestic hot water or heating purposes.

In the case of the **passive** (Trombe) wall, the aim is to heat a wall positioned behind glass sheeting. The heat from this wall is transferred into the room by conduction through it and then by convection and radiation, and by convection through openings at the top and base of the wall. The convection through the wall openings may be either natural or forced.

Solar heating is not popular in the UK owing to the initial cost, which is greater than that of conventional systems, and the fact that the maximum collection efficiency will only take place during the summer, when heating is not required.

OFF-PEAK ELECTRICITY

When electricity is used as an energy source, it may be purchased in two ways: peak period or off-peak. The peak-period costs are the maximum rates that are paid for a unit of electricity.

A power station generates electricity most economically when it operates for 24 hours per day on full load. As electricity demand is never constant over the day, the changes in consumption have to be balanced by starting up or closing down some of the generators. In order to provide an incentive for customers to use electricity outside the normal peak hours, the Regional Electricity Companies offer cheaper off-peak tariffs, in an attempt to cut costs and smooth out the load.

This cheaper electricity cannot be stored as electricity, and it has to be converted into heat, which is stored either in water or in blocks of concrete.

DISTRICT HEATING

The discussion of heating systems up to now has assumed that only one building is supplied with heat. In practice this is not always the case, as buildings may be spread over a large area, but heated from a central boiler house.

A system that supplies, say, a few multi-storey blocks of flats is called a **group heating** scheme, while one that supplies a district, whole town or city from a central boiler house is called a **district heating** scheme. The UK has about 1 per cent of its total space heating supplied by district heating networks. Typical of these arrangements are airports, car factories and universities, and sometimes parts of towns or cities, as in Nottingham.

Figure 4.28 gives some indication of a district heating system. The heat transfer medium used would be high-temperature hot water. Throughout mainland Europe and the USA, district heating systems are popular; however, they have not been fully developed in the UK. The fuels used are usually those covered earlier in this chapter; however, others may be used, such as waste energy from a industrial process, municipal waste, methane from land-fill sites, or geothermal energy.

The distribution subsystems used for such schemes are single-pipe, two-pipe, three-pipe, or four-pipe distribution. The single-pipe system is used in Russia and the USA. It is supplied from a power station, used to supply heating and domestic hot water (DHW) and then run to waste.

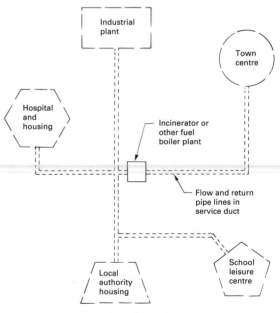

All pipe runs to have expansion bellows and anchors

Figure 4.28   A district heating layout

The two-pipe system is used to supply both the water for space heating and DHW. The pipes are oversized for the DHW required during the summer (Figure 4.29 shows the two-pipe arrangement).

The three-pipe system (Figure 4.30) has two flow mains, one for space heating and one for DHW; the third pipe is a common return for both heating and DHW. The three-pipe system is more expen-sive to install than the two pipe; it does, however, have the advantage of flexibility and savings in mains heat loss and pumping costs during the summer.

In the four-pipe system (Figure 4.31) both the space heating and domestic hot water heating origi-nate in the boiler house; the DHW is stored in the heat exchangers. The pipes are the heating flow and return, and domestic hot water flow and return.

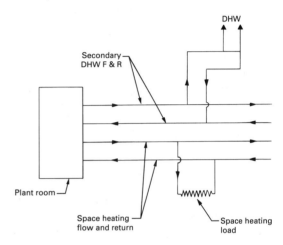

Figure 4.31 Four-pipe district heating system

The above diagrams are simplified as the methods of mixing control are not shown.

COMBINED HEAT AND POWER

In the generation of electricity, a lot of waste heat is produced, which is rejected to the atmosphere, making the overall efficiency of the process low. By using this waste heat for space heating as well as the generated electricity, the process efficiency can be improved.

This process can be carried out from steam plant, diesel generators or gas turbines.

QUESTIONS

1 'Space heating is required in buildings for a variety of reasons.' Discuss this statement.
2 Describe the factors that influence the thermal comfort of a person in a space.

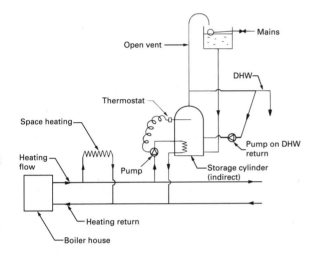

Figure 4.29 Two-pipe district heating system

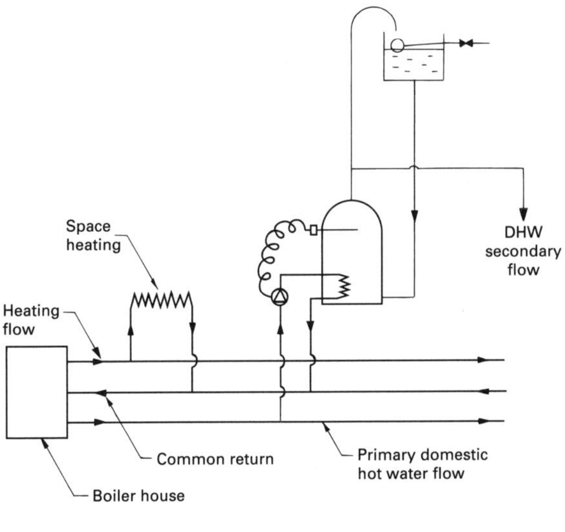

Figure 4.30 Three-pipe district heating system

3 What is the difference between local heating and space heating?

4 Define each of the following terms:
   (a) utilization subsystem;
   (b) distribution subsystem;
   (c) the energy conversion subsystem;
   (d) the control subsystem.

5 With the aid of neat annotated sketches describe the modes of heat transfer that take place from:
   (a) radiators;
   (b) convectors;
   (c) floor-warming systems.

6 For which commercial/industrial applications would you select the following systems?
   (a) an air curtain;
   (b) low surface temperature radiators;
   (c) unit heaters;
   (d) high-level radiant heaters;
   (e) a pipe coil system.

7 What factors influence the selection of a heat emitter for a space?

8 Why is the steel panel radiator not a radiator in the true sense of the word?

9 With the aid of neat annotated sketches, show **two** methods by which solid fuel may be burnt.

10 With the aid of neat annotated sketches, show **one** method that is used for the burning of gas and oil fuel.

11 Discuss the factors that have to be considered in ensuring that the combustion of a fuel is carried out in an efficient manner.

12 Using neat sketches describe the construction and operation of **three** different types of boiler as used in heating engineering.

13 Write brief notes on the origin and use of solid, liquid and gaseous fuels.

14 Discuss **three** different methods by which electricity is used for the heating of buildings.

15 What is the difference between a boiler and a heat generator?

16 What factors have to be considered in the design of a flue for solid or liquid fuel? How do these differ from the flue required for the combustion products of a gaseous fuel?

17 Discuss the following statement: 'The provision of an adequate supply of air for combustion is of prime importance.'

18 What is the difference between a thermosiphonic flow heating system and an accelerated circuit?

19 With the aid of neat diagrams, show the difference between **two** different one-pipe heating systems, and **four** different **two**-pipe systems. State the applications and advantages of each.

20 What is the difference between an open LTHW heating system and a closed system?

21 In what circumstances would you use a HTHW system? Explain in what way its layout is different from those described in Question 20.

22 In what way does a micro-bore system differ from a small-bore system of heating?

23 State **three** reasons why it is necessary to control heating systems.

24 Discuss the merits of a solar panel system over a passive wall system.

25 Define the following terms relating to district heating:
   (a) group heating;
   (b) district heating;
   (c) one-pipe system;
   (d) two-pipe system;
   (e) three-pipe system;
   (f) four-pipe system;
   (g) combined heat and power.
   Use sketches to illustrate your answers.

REFERENCES

1 Physiological principles and thermal comfort, *ASHRAE Fundamentals Handbook*, SI edition (1993) Chapter 8
2 CIBSE Guide AI *Environmental criteria for design* (1986)
3 CIBSE Guide A2 *Weather and solar data* (1982)
4 CIBSE Guide A9 *Estimation of plant capacity* (1983)
5 Randall McMullan, *Environmental Science in Buildings*, Macmillan (1992)
6 BS 6880 : Parts 1–3: *1988 Code of practice for low temperature hot water heating*
7 *Ibid.*, Part 2 Section 3
8 *Ibid.*, Part 1 Section 3; Part 2 Section 4
9 *Ibid.*, Part 2 Section 5
10 *Ibid.*, Part 2 Section 6
11 BS 779 : 1989 *Specification for cast iron boilers for central heating up to 44 kW*
12 BS 2790 : 1992 *Specification for the design of shell boilers*
13 BS 1113 : 1992 *Specification for the design of water tube and steam generators*
14 BS 1894 : 1992 *Specification for the design of electrode boilers*
15 CIBSE Guide B 13 *Combustion systems* (1986); CIBSE Guide C 5 *Fuels and combustion* (1976)
16 BS 749 : 1969 and CP 3000 : 1955 *Specification for underfeed stokers*
17 BS 799 : Parts 1–8 : 1991 *Oil burning equipment*
18 BS 5885 : Parts 1 and 2 : 1988 *Automatic gas burners*

5 VENTILATION, AIR CONDITIONING AND REFRIGERATION

VENTILATION

Ventilation is required in buildings for many different reasons [1]. We shall confine our discussion to that required for domestic and commercial applications, industrial applications being outside the scope of this book.

Ventilation is necessary for the following reasons:

- to provide adequate oxygen to support life;
- to remove body odours by dilution;
- to reduce the bacteria count, by providing fresh air into the space;
- to reduce any toxic gases, vapours and dusts;
- to remove explosive gases and dusts;
- to ensure that adequate combustion air is provided to any combustion process;
- to lower the moisture content in the air, thus reducing the risk of condensation and mould growth;
- to add to or remove heat from the space.

The above factors can be linked together under the following headings:

- health ventilation;
- comfort ventilation;
- structural heating or cooling.

Ventilation can be achieved by the following methods:

- natural ventilation;
- mechanical extract – induced inlet;
- mechanical input – forced extract;
- mechanical inlet – mechanical extract.

We shall discuss each of these in detail.

Natural ventilation [2]

This is the usual method of ventilation in domestic dwellings and many small office buildings in the UK. New European standards, however, may result in more buildings requiring mechanical ventilation systems before the end of the 1990s.

The term **natural ventilation** relates to the air flow in a building that is caused by three natural factors:

(1) temperature differences (thermal density) between the inside and the outside of the building;
(2) wind forces around the building;
(3) a combination of (1) and (2).

Natural ventilation has the advantage that no power supply is required: hence there are no fans and maintenance costs. It has the disadvantage that, during the summer months, the temperature difference between the inside and outside is small, and with low wind forces will result in poor ventilation when it is most required. During the winter months, however, the temperature difference between indoors and outdoors is high, with corresponding high wind forces, resulting in high ventilation rates and high rates of heat loss.

It is not possible to design a system according to a given natural ventilation rate, as this will vary with weather conditions. The cold outdoor air has a greater density, for a given volume, than the warmer indoor air. This density difference causes the cold dense air to enter through low-level openings, displacing the warmer indoor air and creating air changes. The displaced warmer air escapes through high-level openings (see Figure 5.1). Ventilation caused by this method is commonly called the **stack effect**. The greater the distance between the low-level inlets and the high-level outlets, the greater the resulting air change rate will be.

The science of building aerodynamics considers the influence of wind forces over buildings and the associated mechanics of fluids: these are complex in nature and will not be considered here. It will be sufficient to briefly consider Figure 5.2, which shows how wind passing over a building will produce

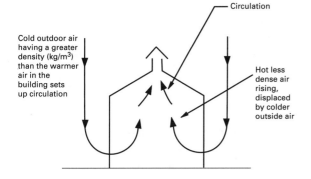

Figure 5.1   The stack effect

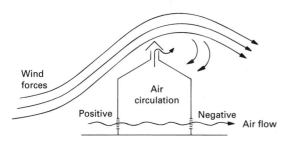

Figure 5.2   Wind forces on a building. *Note*: Actual air flow will be a combination of stack and wind effect

a positive pressure on one side, and a negative pressure on the other. It is this pressure difference that produces air flow through openings. The combined wind and stack effects will vary with the seasons.

Mechanical extract, induced input

The second method of ventilating a building uses an extractor fan, creating a negative pressure within the space. With this method a set flow rate can be achieved, as the fan will overcome the stack and wind effects: hence the system is not at the mercy of the weather. This system causes the inside of the building to be held at a negative pressure, so air will be drawn in from outside or from surrounding spaces that are at a higher pressure.

A space may need to be held at negative pressure, as in lavatories, kitchens and process areas, for example. In such cases air will flow into the negative-pressure zone: hence odours or toxic gases will not escape to other areas. The fan, with its running and maintenance costs, makes this system more expensive than the natural method.

Figure 5.3 shows a typical arrangement of this method of ventilation.

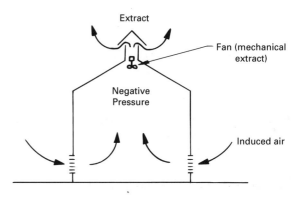

Figure 5.3   Mechanical extract, induced input

Mechanical input, forced extract

If heating is provided, this is known as a **plenum system**. This is a ducted system, which may provide air to a space in one or more of the following conditions:

- untreated air (no filter);
- tempered air by means of a heater battery (heated to near room conditions);
- warm air at a temperature high enough to take care of the fabric and ventilation losses from the building.

With air being forced into the space the pressure is positive: hence all leakages are outwards.

More sophisticated applications of a pressurized system, combined with a suitable extractor, are found in hospital operating theatres. The positive pressure produced by sterile air entering the room ensures that all leakages are outwards. This outward leakage ensures that contaminated air at a lower pressure in the surrounding rooms will not enter the space.

Figure 5.4 shows a typical plenum system.

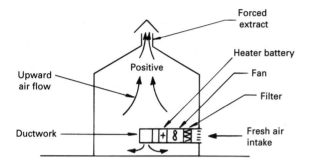

Figure 5.4 A typical plenum system (mechanical input, forced extract)

Mechanical input, mechanical extract

The final method of ventilation is that in which a powered extract and input system are provided. The nature of the pressure produced in this instance depends on the rate of extraction to input, or vice versa. It is no use if the input fans are handling the same amount of air as the extract fans, as this situation will result in a neutral condition, with the disadvantages of the natural system.

Figure 5.5 shows a typical layout of this type of system. From the foregoing statements the advantages and disadvantages of such a system are obvious.

This section has considered methods of ventilation. This should not be considered as being the same as methods of air distribution, which are now discussed.

METHODS OF AIR DISTRIBUTION [3]

When air is supplied to a space by means of a fan forcing it along the ductwork, it has to be distributed into the space without causing draughts, noise, or poor air distribution which would result in stagnant conditions in the space.

Many variations of the following air distribution methods are possible.

Upward ventilation

This arrangement is suited for warm air, as on leaving the grille, hot air will rise. If this air is too hot, it will rise rapidly, and the jet will not reach the middle of the room. Therefore, the leaving velocity and temperature from the grille are critical. If the velocity is too high, the occupants will experience draughts, while if it is too low the occupants in the middle of the room may not receive adequate fresh air. Hence the arrangement shown in Figure 5.6a is not suitable for wide halls. This problem is overcome by using the layout shown in Figure 5.6b.

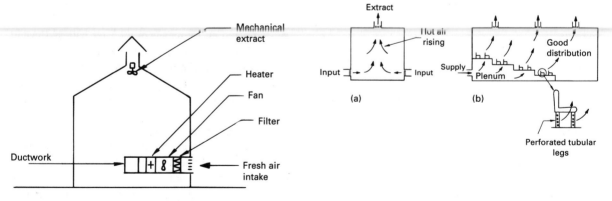

Figure 5.6 Upward ventilation: (a) narrow room; (b) large hall

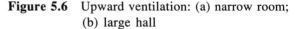

Figure 5.5 Mechanical input, mechanical extract

Downward systems

Air-conditioning systems use this method, as the cooler dense air supplied from high level will drop to low level, picking up the space heat gains before extraction at low level.

It is essential that the entering air is no more than, say, 9 °C cooler than the room air, for if it is, the cold air will drop, causing complaints from the occupants. Full use is made of ceiling diffusers, which ensure that the cold air spreads out over a wide area before dropping. Perforated ceilings may be used, with the ceiling void being the plenum chamber.

A typical downward system is shown in Figure 5.7.

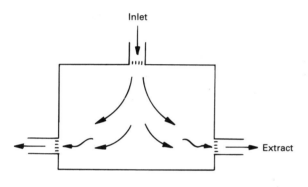

Figure 5.7 Downward system

The arrangements shown in Figure 5.8 are used in industrial halls or auditorias. Clean rooms have complex systems, using laminar flow to ensure that the room is fully ventilated. Full use is made of long jet throws, which entrain room air. Care has

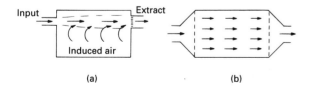

(a)   (b)

Figure 5.8 Crosswise ventilation: (a) jet; (b) laminar flow

to be taken that the air velocity envelope in the occupied zone is in the 0.2–0.25 m/s range, to avoid draughts.

Mixed upward – downward system

The working of this system is shown in Figure 5.9, from which it will be seen that good air mixing takes place. Care has to be taken to ensure that the high-level inlets and extract are positioned so that short-circuiting of the air does not occur.

The low-level extract is normally about 25 per cent of the total extract rate, the actual value being selected to suit the design conditions.

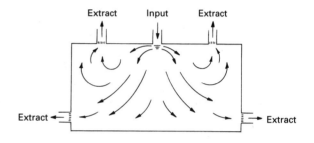

Figure 5.9 Mixed upward–downward system

AIR CHANGE RATE [4]

At the beginning of this chapter, the reasons for ventilation and four methods of ventilation were considered. In heat loss and heat gain studies, consideration is given to the amount of air infiltration that takes place into the space. This may be taken as being a certain number of air changes per hour. For mechanical ventilation, a reasonably accurate figure can be used. However, for natural ventilation the actual value will vary with the wind and thermal forces.

The rate of air interchange can also be determined by selecting the amount of fresh air (litres/second) required per person, or the amount of fresh air per m² of floor area. Values range from 5 l/s to 25 l/s per person, or 0.8–20 l/s per m² of floor area; These are obtained from BS 5925, which is the *Code of Practice for Ventilation*.

The appropriate value relates to activity and whether smoking takes place. It includes the oxygen consumed in breathing, adequate air to dilute the carbon dioxide, and body odours. Table A.4.12 in the *CIBSE Guide A4* gives empirical values for air infiltration for buildings on normal sites in winter. These values range from 0.25 to 5 air changes per hour for different types of building.

The rate of heat loss due to ventilation is obtained from

$$Q_v = 0.33NV(t_{ai} - t_{ao})$$

where Q_v is the heat requirement due to ventilation, N is the number of air changes per hour, V is the room volume (m^3), t_{ai} is the inside air temperature (°C), and t_{ao} is the outside temperature (°C). The constant of 0.33 is the ratio of the specific heat capacity of the air (1.01 kJ/kg °C) and the density of the air (1.2 kg/m^3) divided by 3600 (seconds in 1 hour).

When high ventilation rates are required, mechanical ventilation is necessary; for example, commercial kitchens may require 20 or more air changes per hour. The higher the ventilation rate, the greater are the heating or cooling costs.

EXAMPLE

The air supply to a conference room is 240 l/s (0.24 m^3/s). The room is 8 m × 4 m in plan with a 3 m ceiling height. Determine the number of air changes that take place.

Answer

First, determine the volume of the room: $V = 8 \times 4 \times 3 = 96\ m^3$. The basic equation for determining the air change rate is:

$$N = 3600\ \frac{Q}{V}$$

$$= 3600 \times \frac{0.24}{96} = 9 \text{ air changes per hour}$$

This indicates that the air in the room changes 9 times per hour: that is, nine volumes of outside air are brought into the space and expelled every hour.

The method of inlet and extract will influence the efficiency of this air interchange. Good distribution will ensure that there are no stagnant spaces in the room, while poor distribution will result in stagnant pockets remaining in the room.

AIR-CONDITIONING SYSTEMS

The simple ventilation systems considered above, which merely use heated air, are not suitable in may cases, and therefore air-conditioning systems have to be considered.

The selection of a suitable air-conditioning system for a building is a complex matter, and no hard and fast rules are available. It is up to the designer with a knowledge of the building use and fabric type to determine the most economical system. Air-conditioning installation costs for a given space may be *five times* the cost of a simple heating system. The running and maintenance costs of such a system are also considerably higher.

Air conditioning may be required for the following reasons.

- Thermal comfort of the occupants will increase productivity, improve the health of the workers and reduce absenteeism.
- The space conditions may need to be controlled for a particular process. In this case human comfort may not be met.
- Set conditions of air purity, moisture content, and temperature may need to be maintained. This is necessary in clean rooms, hospital operating theatres, museums, stores for old manuscripts, computer rooms and the like.

Air conditioning of a space is necessary if space conditions have to be held at a constant value, regardless of the external conditions. An example would be a computer room, which has to be held at fixed temperature and moisture content regardless of the external conditions.

Consider a room that has to be held at 20 °C when the external air temperature is 28 °C. Without air cooling the space cannot be held at 20 °C, because the interior and exterior heat gains mean that the space temperature would always be higher than the external conditions.

Ventilation will remove some of these internal gains. The quantity of air necessary for cooling will vary, depending on many factors. If a large temperature difference exists between the supply air and the room air, only a small air quantity will be required; if a small temperature difference between the supply and room air exists, a larger air quantity becomes necessary. The air quantity has a direct effect on the size of the ductwork and hence the space taken up in horizontal or vertical runs. The heat gains to be considered are:

- **sensible heat** – the gains from occupants, lights, machines, processes, infiltration, conduction and solar, through the windows and other parts of the fabric;
- **latent heat** – the moisture gains from infiltration, occupants and processes.

The sensible gains have a direct influence on the air temperature, while the latent gains do not directly influence the surrounding temperature, but influence the moisture content in the space.

It is essential to ensure that a simple ventilation system is not classed as an air-conditioning system. An air-conditioning system must be capable of achieving the following:

- filtering (air purity);
- heating;
- cooling (without moisture removal);
- humidification (moisture addition);
- dehumidifying (moisture removal);
- distributing the air within the space without creating discomfort or stagnant pockets (this must be related to the methods considered in the section on air distribution).

A simple ventilation system is assumed to be capable only of filtering, heating and distributing the air in the space.

Psychrometrics

In any study of air conditioning a knowledge of psychrometrics is necessary. This considers the behaviour of air when heated, cooled, humidified or dehumidified.

The study of psychrometry involves the nature of the moisture and heat content of air under different atmospheric conditions. The gas laws and the associated thermodynamic principles are outside the scope of this book. The study of psychrometrics makes use of the CIBSE *Properties of Humid Air*, Books C1 and 2, as well as the psychrometric chart, which allows a visual understanding of the air-conditioning cycle.

The following conditions are plotted on a psychrometric chart:

- dry-bulb temperature (°C);
- wet-bulb temperature (°C);
- percentage saturation (%);
- moisture content (kg/kg);
- dew-point temperature (°C);
- specific enthalpy (kJ/kg);
- specific volume (m³/kg).

If two or more of the constituent conditions of an air sample are known it is possible to determine any of the others from the chart.

Figure 5.10 shows a simple cycle of how winter outside air at a condition of say −5 °C and 20 per cent saturation has to be conditioned in order for it to reach a room condition of 20 °C and 50 per cent saturation.

In heating the air from −5 °C to 20 °C the percentage saturation decreases, but the moisture content remains constant. If the air entered the room at this moisture condition, static electricity and sore throats would result. In order to get the air to room conditions it is necessary to heat the air beyond 20 °C and spray chilled water into this warm air to cool it, and add moisture.

During the summer months the outside air temperature may be 28 °C with 80 per cent saturation, containing about 0.02 kg/kg of moisture.

Figure 5.12 shows the air path in this case. As can be seen, the air is first cooled to its dew-point, then further cooling extracts the moisture.

In order to obtain accurate values the CIBSE tables have to be used. The previous figures show only hypothetical cycles; in practice, they are more complicated than this.

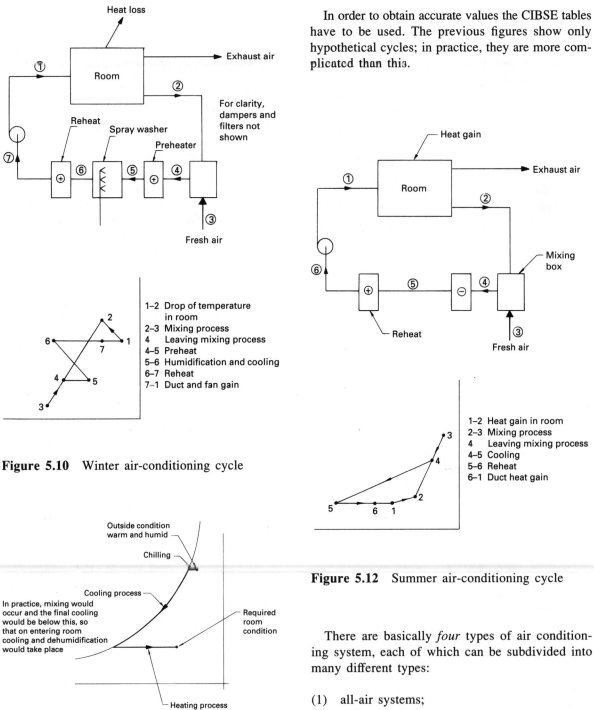

1–2 Drop of temperature in room
2–3 Mixing process
4 Leaving mixing process
4–5 Preheat
5–6 Humidification and cooling
6–7 Reheat
7–1 Duct and fan gain

Figure 5.10   Winter air-conditioning cycle

1–2 Heat gain in room
2–3 Mixing process
4 Leaving mixing process
4–5 Cooling
5–6 Reheat
6–1 Duct heat gain

Figure 5.12   Summer air-conditioning cycle

Figure 5.11   Psychrometric process

There are basically *four* types of air conditioning system, each of which can be subdivided into many different types:

(1) all-air systems;
(2) air/water systems;
(3) all-water systems (2 and 3 may be grouped together);
(4) unitary systems.

All-air system

This system provides latent cooling and sensible cooling and heating to the conditioned space. Once the heating and cooling requirements in the space are known, the capacity of the thermal exchange units, together with the necessary air volume, are used to design a system that will meet the space requirements.

Figure 5.13 shows the general arrangements of a central system. For large loads this may be a system built up on site; for smaller loads it may be a central air handler, which is delivered to the site as a self-contained unit, and consists of an outer case enclosing the refrigerator, cooling coil, filter and heating coil. Typical applications of the all-air system are large open spaces such as banking halls and lecture theatres.

When the system is used for several rooms it is essential to ensure that the heating or cooling loads are similar in magnitude; if not, a terminal reheater battery is fitted to the air supply at each outlet to allow individual regulation of space conditions. A control damper may be used to vary the air supply; this arrangement is called a **variable air volume** (VAV) system. The air flow rate is controlled by a thermostat operating a control motor on the damper. This arrangement has the disadvantage that the air supply may be reduced to such a low value that insufficient fresh air is supplied to the space.

The **single-duct system** has one major problem, in that the air supply is at set temperature and moisture conditions. This is satisfactory for a large rooms; however, for numerous rooms with varying sensible and latent heat gains, thermal discomfort will result from the fixed air quality.

The shortcomings of the single-duct system can be overcome by the use of the **dual-duct system**. This is more expensive than the single-duct system, but allows better control of the air conditions within rooms that have wide-ranging demands of heating and cooling.

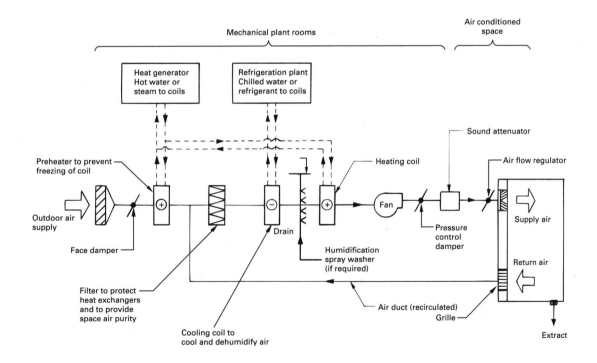

Figure 5.13 Air conditioning: all-air system

Air flow in the two supply ducts may be at a high velocity of 10–30 m/s, which is greater than in the single-duct system. This allows much smaller ducts to be used, resulting in smaller vertical and horizontal service ducts, and giving savings in the ceiling void depth and floor space necessary to accommodate these ducts. The high-velocity system requires more costly fans to overcome the extra frictional resistance, extra power running costs, and acoustic treatment to stop noise breakout into the space. The two ducts are required to allow one to carry chilled air while the other carries hot air (see Figure 5.14). During the cooling cycle, the hot duct carries a blend of fresh and recirculated air, while the cold air duct carries the chilled, dehumidified air. The hot and cold air are mixed together in the mixing box, the proportions of the mix determined by the dampers that are controlled by the room thermostat.

During the winter, the cold duct carries fresh and recirculated air, while the hot duct conveys the warm air to take care of the heat loss. This type of system can respond rapidly to heating or cooling load fluctuation.

The reader may encounter the terms constant volume (CV), re-heat, variable air volume (VAV), multi-zone units and rooftop units; these are all air systems.

Air–water systems

As water has a specific heat capacity about four times greater than that of air, and a density about 833 times greater, it is of benefit to deal with part of the heat gain by using chilled water. This water is supplied to terminal units in the conditioned rooms. This allows less building space to be taken up by large ductwork, as the chilled water pipes are considerably smaller than the ductwork necessary for the same cooling duty.

As with the all-air systems, many different variations are in use. These include;

- perimeter induction units;
- fan coil units;
- chilled ceilings.

Only the the first two methods will be considered.

Induction unit [5]

This system is cheaper to install than the all-air system, and is well suited for multi-room applications.

Fresh air is provided from the central plant. The total air handled with the water cooling or heating is considerably less than that handled in the all-air system. Most of the heating and cooling, humidification and dehumidification is dealt with in the central plant room, with final adjustments at the terminal unit.

Primary high-velocity fresh air in the duct enters the induction unit, and the operating air pressure injects the air through induction nozzles. The high-velocity jets create an **induction effect**: a suction effect within the unit case. This pressure reduction induces room air (**secondary**) over a filter into the unit. Depending on requirements, as this

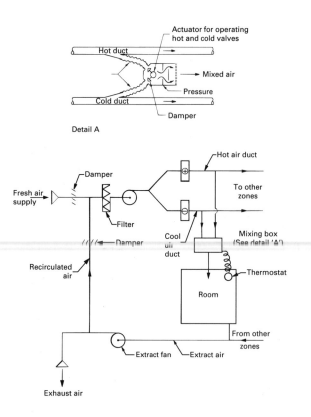

Figure 5.14 Air conditioning: dual-duct system

air passes through the coil it is either heated or cooled.

Depending on the velocity of the air in the jet, the quantity of air induced may be three or four times the volume flow rate of the primary air from the plant. The induction rate (secondary air) can be altered by changing the nozzles, or by means of a damper. The heating/cooling coil in the unit is fed with either hot or chilled water, while the piping may be two-pipe, three-pipe or four-pipe.

The **two-pipe system** is capable only of heating or cooling, and a changeover date from summer (cooling) to winter (heating). The **three-pipe system** is not an energy-efficient system and would not normally be used. It has a blending valve connected to the hot and chilled water, the third pipe being the common return. The **four-pipe system** is the best arrangement; however, it is the most costly, as it consists of chilled water and heating flow and return pipes. Figure 5.15 shows a typical arrangement of a four-pipe system. The other type of system listed under the air–water system is the fan coil unit.

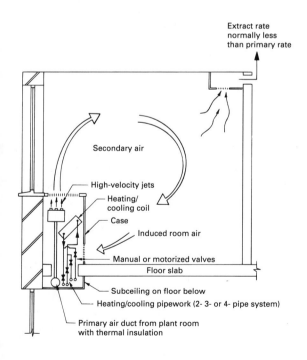

Figure 5.15 Four-pipe perimeter induction unit

Fan coil unit [6]

In areas where the heat gains or losses are high, fan coil units are well suited. This type of unit is located in the false ceiling of the room, as shown in Figure 5.16.

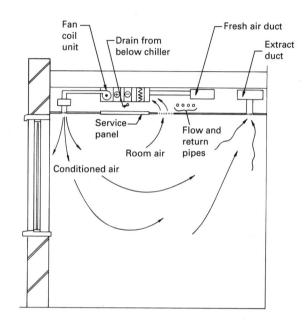

Figure 5.16 Fan coil unit

This system filters the room air, and a service panel is required below the unit to allow for service of the fan, filter, coil and controls. The extracted air from the space, in this and all the other systems, can be taken through ventilated luminaires. This arrangement removes the heat gain from the light at source and reduces the cooling load required for the space. The supply duct carries only the fresh air quantity.

Unitary system

Such systems are very common for small and medium-sized systems. They are self-contained, air-cooled, room air conditioners. A unitary system comprises a direct expansion air cooler coil, a supply air fan, a hermetic refrigeration compressor, an air-cooled condenser and a condenser fan. A drip tray with a drain is fitted below the cooling coil and a filter of the throwaway type is placed in front of the cooler coil.

Unitary systems may be of the window unit type or the split system type, which allows the condensing unit to be separated from the air cooler coil and located up to about 15 m from it. This arrangement allows the unit to be quieter than the self-contained, air-cooled type; it is more costly, however.

The cooling capacities of self-contained units range from about 1.5 to 9 kW, the latter having a power consumption of about 3 kW. The anticipated life of the unit is from about 3 to 10 years; air distribution from them is poor.

The split system has a cooling range of up to about 500 kW. The acoustic environment within the conditioned space from air- and structure-borne sound is kept to set levels.

BASIC REFRIGERATION PROCESS

As the boiler (heat generator) is the heart of a heating system, so the refrigerator is the heart of an air-conditioning system. The purpose of refrigeration in air-conditioning systems is to remove heat gain from the space, hence lowering the temperature. Refrigeration can be provided by a number of means, such as the vapour compression cycle and the absorption cycle. The vapour compression cycle is the method in common use. Before considering the thermodynamic cycle, it is essential to understand a few thermodynamic relationships.

The first of these is **saturated vapour temperature** (SVT). This is the technical term for what is commonly termed **boiling point**. As the reader will be aware, water boils at 100 °C, but it is essential to add to this statement 'but only at **atmospheric pressure**': hence at a **standard atmosphere** of 101.325 kPa, water boils at 100 °C. The saturated vapour temperature is the temperature at which a liquid evaporates: in other words, changes from a liquid to a vapour. It is also the temperature at which it will change back from a vapour to a liquid. This reversal of the evaporating process is known as **condensing**. To evaporate a liquid, large quantities of heat energy are required, while in condensing the vapour large quantities of heat are given up.

If the pressure on the surface of a liquid is increased, the SVT is also increased, and conversely if the pressure on a liquid surface is decreased the SVT is decreased.

Considering water, if the pressure on its surface is greater than standard atmospheric pressure, its SVT (boiling point) will be greater than 100 °C, as is the case with a steam boiler, whereas if the pressure is less than atmospheric, the boiling point will be less than 100 °C.

Water could be used as a refrigerant; however, the pressure reduction necessary to obtain low temperatures would be great, resulting in large power requirements and massive containing plant to withstand the maximum and minimum pressures. Hence water is not used for the vapour compression cycle.

Various fluids with low boiling points are the refrigerants used in the vapour compression cycle. The ideal fluid should be: non-toxic, non-corrosive, non-explosive, cheap, pollution-free, non-oil-reactive, should have high specific heat and low working pressures, and should not require a large power input and expensive plant.

The fluids used in the past were the **chlorofluorocarbons**, which are the methane series refrigerants (CFC), but once this gas is liberated to the atmosphere, it causes two serious environmental effects, the breakdown of the ozone layer and the **greenhouse effect**.

A numbering system is used to relate the chemical composition of these refrigerants: for example, R12 (CCl_2F_2) is dichlorodifluoromethane, and R22 ($CHClF_2$) is monochlorodifluoromethane.

In order to eliminate CFCs, an international ban was agreed at a meeting known as the Montreal Convention, which stipulated that only safe refrigerants, such as hydrofluoroalkane (HFA, manufactured by ICI), were to be used in Europe from 1 January 1995.

Figure 5.17 shows the simplest possible evaporator refrigerator in which HFA could be used. HFA evaporates at −26.22 °C at atmospheric pressure. At first the temperature in the container is the same as the surroundings. For the liquid to evaporate, **latent heat of evaporation** has to be supplied through the container to the liquid. As the liquid evaporates, the temperature of the box and its contents are reduced.

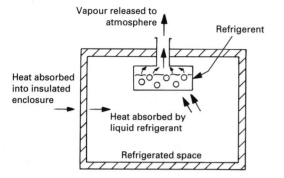

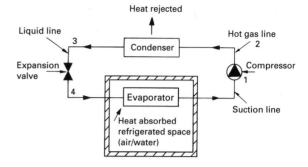

Figure 5.17 The simplest possible evaporation refrigerator, based on boiling of liquid

Figure 5.18 Basic vapour compression refrigeration cycle

The metal container is a heat exchanger, and is known as the **evaporator** for obvious reasons. The temperature at which the refrigerant evaporates in the evaporator is known as the **evaporating temperature**.

The temperature in the container becomes lower, eventually falling near to the HFA boiling temperature. At this stage, the HFA is unable to absorb any more heat from the surroundings, which are at the same temperature.

This type of system will work; it does, however present the following problems.

● It operates with only one evaporating temperature. Hence if a temperature higher or lower than $-26.22\,°C$ is required, there is a problem.
● As the HFA evaporates the refrigerant passes to the atmosphere, wasting an expensive refrigerant and polluting the atmosphere.

To overcome this problem the refrigerant is reclaimed, by arranging a cycle that passes through a condenser to **condense** the vapour back to a liquid. To achieve this a pump (**compressor**) is required; the new arrangement is shown in Figure 5.18 This arrangement, depending on the amount of suction, will allow boiling (evaporation) of the liquid to take place at a wide range of temperatures. From the figure it will be noted that an expansion device (**expansion valve**) is included.

At this stage we shall consider the cycle in its full operation (see Figure 5.18). Line 1 is the suction line, which is a large-diameter pipe, often frosted and at low temperature, and carries the vapour to the suction inlet of the compressor. The vapour is compressed by the compressor to a much higher pressure than that existing in the suction inlet. It leaves the compressor as a hot superheated vapour in line 2. The term 'superheated vapour' indicates that the vapour is heated above its saturated vapour temperature level at that pressure.

This vapour is conveyed in the hot gas line to the condenser. Once it is in the condenser, heat is rejected to the surroundings, and the refrigerant is conveyed in pipe 3, the liquid line, which is a small-diameter pipe at high pressure, to the expansion valve. The difference in pressure between the liquid line and the evaporator forces the liquid through the small orifice of the expansion valve.

As the pressure reduces, some evaporation takes place. The heat absorbed by this evaporation cools the liquid down to the evaporating temperature, and it leaves the expansion device (4) as a mixture of saturated liquid and saturated vapour.

The liquid evaporates in the evaporator, absorbing heat from the surrounding space. The saturated vapour then leaves the evaporator and enters the suction line 1, and the cycle starts all over again. Even though only HFA has been mentioned, this arrangement is common to all types of refrigerants used in the vapour compression cycle.

HEAT PUMPS [7]

The heat pump is a reversible refrigerator which can heat a space in winter, and cool in summer.

Refrigerators and heat pumps work in much the same way, as they have the same parts and working fluids. A refrigerator extracts heat from a source and rejects it to the environment. The heat pump extracts heat from the environment and supplies it at a higher temperature to the enclosure. The source could be a factory, house or an industrial process.

The attraction of the heat pump is the free heat that it makes available. The only energy for which the consumer has to pay is that required to drive the compressor. To this is added the free heat extracted from the environment.

Figure 5.19 shows the arrangement of a typical heat pump. The use of a four-way valve and a bypass on the compressor will make the cycle reversible.

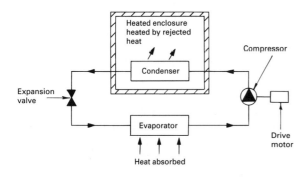

Figure 5.19   Basic heat pump arrangement

Having discussed the basic methods of ventilation, air conditioning and refrigeration systems, we now need to consider the fans, filters and ductwork that these systems require.

FANS

A fan is a mechanical air-moving device that is used in domestic, commercial and industrial ventilation and air-conditioning systems. At this stage only a brief introduction is necessary in order to appreciate the various types in use.

Fan selection

In order to select a fan the following information is needed:

- air volume to be moved (m^3/s);
- fan static pressure required (Pa);
- noise level (dB);
- direct or belt drive;
- air cleanliness, explosive risks and operating temperature;
- power requirements (W).

Fans come in many types and shapes, each one having a specific application.

Axial flow fans

This type of fan creates air flow parallel to the air shaft. The fan may be a low-pressure propeller; there are also duct fans and vane axial fans, which develop a higher pressure.

The simplest fan is the **propeller** type, this form being a typical window or wall fan. It is a simple propeller, usually with three or four blades mounted in a ring or cage. As there is no way of confining the flow, conversion of velocity pressure to static pressure is minimal, and so this type of fan cannot be used to overcome the resistance of ductwork. The operating efficiency is low, owing to the helical and radial motion of the air. Typical applications are domestic and small commercial extraction or input.

By placing a propeller in a duct (a **tube-axial** fan), part of the energy that is wasted in radial motion can be converted into velocity and static pressure. This fan type will operate against slightly higher resistances than a propeller fan, and is sensitive to variations in resistance.

By installing guide vanes either ahead of or following the airfoil shape impeller of a tube-axial fan, the fan becomes known as **vane-axial**. The vanes straighten the helical flow pattern and convert velocity pressure into useful static pressure, thus increasing the efficiency.

Vane axial fans are suitable for pressures up to 2 kPa, and are competitive with centrifugal fans; at pressures below 1 kPa, they are quieter than centrifugal fans. They have the advantage of simplicity in that they can be mounted in a duct, and are space saving when compared with centrifugal fans.

Centrifugal fans

These are used for supply and extract in all types of ventilation and air-conditioning systems.

The air enters enters to the shaft, turns through 90°, passes between the blades of the fan wheel, and discharges at right-angles to the inlet. The velocity and static pressure are increased principally by centrifugal force. The case or scroll is spiral in shape. Centrifugal fans are classified as radial, forward curved, or backward curved, according to the blade shape.

Radial blade fans are also known as **paddle-wheel** fans. The rotors have between 5 and 12 blades, which are ruggedly fabricated; they are used for handling dirty air or dust.

They are noisy, and require a large power input for a given duty compared with other fan types. The maximum static efficiency is about 65–70 per cent, which is much lower than for other centrifugal type fans.

They will handle air volumes up to 50 m³/s at temperatures of 540°C and pressures up to 5 kPa.

The **forward-curved blade** fan has a large number of closely spaced shallow blades. The forward-curved blade builds up a high velocity, which is partly converted into static pressure by the scroll. The normal pressure range is 500–1000 Pa; however, higher pressures may be obtained. Maximum efficiency is about 70 per cent.

The power requirement rises rapidly with increasing volume.

The **backward-curved blade** fan produces non-overloading characteristics. The wheel consists of a few flat, curved or aerofoil-shaped blades. The blade shape allows the air to follow the blade, even at high volume flow rates. Consequently, at high flow rates the static pressures and efficiency are high. The power requirement decreases as the volume approaches its maximum (no closed dampers): this is known as the **wide open** condition. As the blades are backward curved, higher speeds are required for a given duty than are necessary for other types, hence a rugged construction is required. The noise level is high.

Table 5.1 *Comparison of fan types*

	Backward	Radial	Forward	Vane-axial	Propeller
First cost	H	M	L	L	VL
Efficiency	H	M	M	H	VL
Stability of operation	G	G	P	G	P
Space required	M	M	MS	S	S
Noise	H	M	L	M	H

Key: H = high; M = medium; MS = medium small; S = small; L = low; VL = very low; G = good; P = poor.

Table 5.1 compares the various fan types; Figure 5.20 gives a basic idea of the shapes of various fan types.

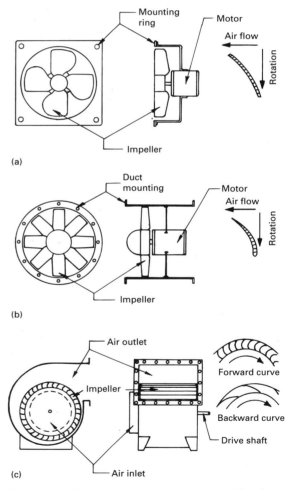

Figure 5.20 Basic fan types: (a) propeller fan; (b) axial flow fan; (c) centrifugal fan

FILTERS

It is essential to clean both the fresh air and the recirculated air in an air-conditioning system. This is required to:

- remove airborne particles, which will stain the internal building surfaces, requiring frequent cleaning and painting;
- remove micro-organisms that cause infection;
- remove gaseous pollutants, which can affect the health of the occupants in the building.

The efficiency of the collection devices used depends upon the use of the space; a hospital operating theatre requires a greater standard of air purity than an office.

The physical size of dust is measured in a unit called the **micrometre** (μm), which is 1×10^{-6} metre. The term 'micron' is also used, but should be avoided as it is a non-SI term.

Particles less than 2.5 μm in diameter are classed as being **fine**, while particles above this diameter are called **coarse**. Particulate matter greater than 10 μm is considered to be non-respirable dust, and as such will not enter the lungs. Various filter types are used to collect the particulate matter in the ventilation ductwork; their selection depends on the collection efficiency required. Filters collect particles by three mechanisms:

- **Impaction**: This occurs when particles have so much inertia that they collide with the elemental fibres of a filter, rather than move round them.
- **Interception**: In this case the particles do not actually hit the fibres, but they come so close that they are caught in the low-velocity air layer that surrounds each fibre.
- **Diffusion**: This occurs when small particles move randomly backwards and forwards within the filter bed due to collisions with the air molecules (Brownian motion).

As air flows through a porous medium (filter), the particulate matter suspended in it will be trapped in the filter medium. The most common of filters are woven, felted or pressed fabric. The domestic vacuum cleaner uses either a paper or a cloth filter to trap the dust. Woven metal is used as a filter for oil in a car engine.

Filtering devices are classed as disposable or reusable. **Disposable** filters use inexpensive materials in the form of panels, mats and cartridges. A wide range of materials are used, depending on the application. If high-toxicity particulate matter has to be collected, high-efficiency particulate air (HEPA) filters are used. **Reusable filter elements** have a cleaning mechanism to provide periodic dust removal.

Not all filters are fabric; the very efficient electrostatic filters do not have any fabric in them, but instead rely on giving dust particles a positive electrical charge. These charged particles are then attracted to negatively charged plates.

Carbon filters are used to remove smells from certain processes; they are protected by a standard filter so that they do not become clogged up with dust.

DUCTWORK [8]

The design of ventilation ductwork is a complex matter, as the following factors have to be considered:

- availability of space;
- permitted noise levels;
- degree of duct air leakage;
- location to give the best air diffusion into the room;
- effect of heat losses or gains from or to the duct;
- fire and smoke control;
- initial costs;
- system operating cost (frictional loss);
- balancing requirements;
- need to carry the correct quantity of air.

Unlike electrical cables or pipework, ductwork takes up a lot of valuable floor space in buildings. If corners are cut to save floor or ceiling space, a noisy environment, high operating cost and, possibly, an insufficient air supply will result.

The duct shape (square, rectangular, round or oval), and the number and type of bends and fittings in a duct run, influence the resistance in the duct network. This resistance has a direct influence on the running costs of fans.

Systems are designed by the use of computers, tables or charts, to ensure a cost-effective system (see CIBSE Technical Memorandum TM 8 *Design notes for ductwork* [8]).

The standards of manufacture influence the operating pressures. Ductwork is normally manufactured from galvanized mild steel sheet; however, plastic, aluminium and stainless steel are also used. For main runs the ductwork is rigid, although connections to diffusers may be manufactured from flexible material. The ductwork runs have dampers to control the air flow rate, and fire dampers are fitted.

Noise transmission in ductwork can present problems, so sound attenuators are sometimes fitted. Connections to fans are separated by means of flexible connections. For rectangular ducts the aspect ratio is critical in order to reduce drumming.

At the room end of the ductwork, the air terminal devices are fitted. It is essential to ensure that these are capable of distributing the correct air quantity in the manner required.

QUESTIONS

1 Explain in about 1000 words why ventilation is required in a building.
2 With the aid of neat annotated sketches discuss the various methods of ventilation that can be used in buildings.
3 What is meant by the following terms?
   (a) stack effect;
   (b) wind effect;
   (c) positive ventilation;
   (d) negative ventilation;
   (e) air change rate.
4 Discuss with the aid of neat sketches **five** different methods of air distribution that may be found in commercial or industrial buildings.
5 Discuss three methods by which the required air change rate in a building may be determined.
6 A room of volume of 150 m³ is found to have

3 air changes per hour. The heating system is only just capable of holding the space air temperature during winter design conditions. Staff complaints are made regarding the lack of air freshness in the space. It is decided to increase the air change rate to 6 per hour to overcome this problem. If the winter outside design is −5 °C when the room design is 20 °C, determine the extra heat input required to take care of the additional air change rate.
7 Discuss the reasons why a simple ventilation system may not be suitable for a particular application, and air conditioning must be used.
8 What is the difference between the sensible and latent heat of air?
9 Why is it necessary to understand the psychrometric cycle when designing air-conditioning systems?
10 By means of neat annotated sketches show **four** different types of air conditioning system that are in common use.
11 Compare the operation of a heat pump with the simple vapour compression cycle.

REFERENCES

1 *HVAC Applications* ASHRAE (1991) Chapters 1–28. Comfort Air Conditioning, etc.
2 CIBSE Guide A 4 *Natural ventilation* (1986)
3 *Air Diffusion Guide* 2nd edn, Heating Ventilating and Air Conditioning Manufacturers Association (1988)
4 BS 5925 : 1991 *Code of practice for ventilating principles and designing for natural ventilation*
5 BS 4954 : Parts 1 and 2: 1987 *Methods of testing and rating induction units for air distribution systems*
6 BS 4856 : Parts 1–5: 1983 *Methods for testing and rating terminal reheat units for air distribution*
7 BS 7326 : Parts 1 and 2: 1990 *Specification for the rating of heat pumps*
8 *Design notes for ductwork* CIBSE Technical Memorandum TM 8 (1990)

6 ELECTRICAL SERVICES FOR BUILDINGS

Before considering the methods of electrical distribution in a building it will be prudent to consider briefly the nature of electricity, and the methods of generation and distribution of electricity.

ELECTRICITY

The study of electricity is complex, as electron flow and the associated positive and negative charges have to be considered, so a detailed study would be beyond the scope of the book. However, before starting on electrical services it is necessary for basic electrical flow to be understood, in order to appreciate what happens in an electrical supply. This is possible by considering the **hydraulic–electrical analogy**, in which water flow in a pipe is related to electrical flow in a conductor. If a path of low resistance is offered to an electrical current, the current will take this easiest path; a path of this nature is known as a short circuit.

Electrical flow can be considered as being akin to water flow in a pipe. With water, flow will take place from a high-level reservoir to a pipe outlet at the bottom of a hill. The height difference or head gives the water potential energy. If the water is allowed to flow down a pipe to a lower level than the reservoir, the resulting velocity will impart enough energy to drive a Pelton wheel, which in turn can operate a shaft. The potential energy in the reservoir is converted into kinetic energy as it leaves the pipe, driving the waterwheel.

Relating the hydraulic system to electricity, the electrical potential can be considered as being analogous to pressure, which causes a flow of electrical current from a place of high potential to one of low potential. The limitation of this analogy must be appreciated, as we must not assume that the current can squirt out of the end of a wire to drive an electric motor!

A conductor of a small cross-section area, for a given flow will produce a large resistance, as would also a small-diameter water pipe, whereas a larger cross-section area conductor, with the same flow, will produce a smaller resistance (pressure drop): the greater the resistance, the greater the heat produced.

The unit of electrical resistance is the **ohm** (Ω); this will allow a current of one **ampere** (A) to pass, when a potential difference of one **volt** (V) is applied.

In practice, multiples of volts are expressed in kilovolts (kV), watts in kW or MW (1000 kW), and 1000 watt hours are known as the kilowatt hour (1 kWh).

Figure 6.1 shows a **simple electrical circuit**. In order for current to flow, a difference in electrical pressure is necessary; this is provided by the generator, which supplies the electromotive force (emf). The unit of electromotive force is the volt (potential difference).

The following governing equations must be understood in the study of electrical engineering.

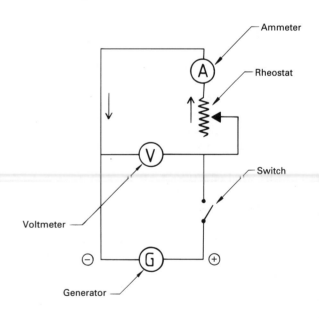

Figure 6.1 Simple electrical circuit

Ohm's law gives the relationship that exists between current voltage and resistance, and is expressed as:

$$I = \frac{V}{R} \qquad (1)$$

where I is the current in amps, V is the voltage in volts, and R is the resistance in ohms.

Power is expressed by:

$$W \text{ (watts)} = V \times I \qquad (2)$$

From Equation (1):

$$V = I \times R \qquad (3)$$

Combining Equations (2) and (3) gives

$$W = I^2 R \qquad (4)$$

Shown in the circuit in Figure 6.1 is a variable resistance (rheostat), a voltmeter, an ammeter and a switch. As the pointer on the rheostat is moved, the circuit resistance can be increased or decreased. The switch can be considered as being the same as an isolating valve in a pumped water circuit. With a closed switch and the generator on, a continuous path of current will flow in the direction of the arrows. The potential difference is measured by means of a voltmeter, and the current flow is measured by the ammeter: the greater the cross-sectional area of the conductors, the smaller the circuit resistance for a given current.

ELECTRICAL GENERATION AND DISTRIBUTION

In the United Kingdom power is generated mainly by fossil fuels, coal, gas, oil and nuclear. Gas turbines as generators are being used in increasing numbers during the first half of the 1990s. A small percentage of the total demand is also produced by: hydroelectric, pumped storage, and wind turbines.

Fossil fuel plants burn pulverized coal or a heavy-grade atomized oil to produce superheated steam in the boilers. This steam is fed to 500 or 600 MW turbine sets in the larger stations. The Drax power station in the Yorkshire coalfields has a nominal capacity of 4000 MW. The steam is delivered to the turbine stop valve at a pressure exceeding 7.0 MPa (70 bar) and temperature of 566 °C. Nuclear power provides about 20 per cent of the UK power requirement. In this case steam is generated by the heat produced by the nuclear reaction taking place within the reactor.

For power stations to be economical, they must operate for 24 hours per day. As the demand for electricity is never constant, changes have to be made by starting and stopping some of the generators. This approach results in a drop in the overall plant efficiency. In an attempt to keep the demand and efficiency as high as possible, off-peak tariffs are offered.

The steam-driven turbine shaft drives the generator, producing electricity at the stator windings, at voltages of up to 23.5 kV. On leaving the generator, the electricity passes to a step-up transformer, where the voltage is boosted to 132, 275, or 400 kV. This voltage increase is necessary to reduce the national grid cable size required to carry a given amperage.

The overhead and underground transmission lines in the UK cover about 7700 km and pass through some 200 substations. Figure 6.2 shows a typical

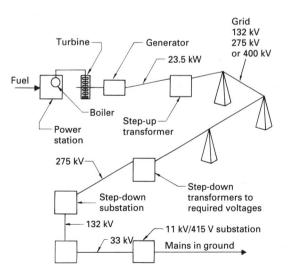

Figure 6.2 Typical electrical distribution system

transmission system, with the voltage reducing from 400 kV to 33 kV.

Electricity in the UK was formally generated by the Central Electricity Generating Board (CEGB), but the Board has been replaced by Power Generation (Power Gen) and National Power. The regional electricity companies obtain power from them and distribute it in their own respective territories. Some companies are now producing their own electricity on a small scale.

A term that often tends to cause confusion to students is that of **three-phase supply**. This refers to an alternating current that continually varies in both magnitude and direction. It consists of three overlapping currents, one in each phase.

In a **single-phase** circuit the electromotive force (emf) undergoes one complete cycle of variation when the conductors in the alternator rotate through opposite magnetic fields set up by magnets. The voltage rises to a maximum positive value then falling to zero before continuing to a maximum negative value, before returning to zero. The number of cycles occurring in one second is termed the **frequency**, the unit of which is the hertz (Hz). The frequency of the UK supply is 50 Hz.

In plotting the emf produced by a single-phase circuit for one complete cycle against a time base, a curve is obtained as shown in Figure 6.3. This waveform approximates to a sine wave.

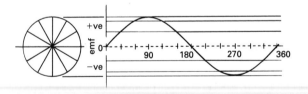

Figure 6.3   Single-phase supply

When three coils are rotated at uniform speed in the magnetic field of an alternator three identical waveforms are obtained. One lags behind the first wave by one-third of a cycle, or 120°, and the other lags by two-thirds or 240°, as indicated in Figure 6.4.

The windings of an alternator producing such a current may have their ends connected together as in Figure 6.5. This arrangement is called a **delta**

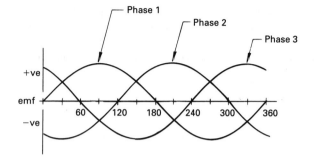

Figure 6.4   Three-phase supply

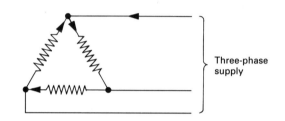

Figure 6.5   Delta connection

or **mesh** connection, giving what is termed a **three-phase, three-wire supply**.

Figure 6.6 shows an alternator in an arrangement known as a **star** connection. In this case, one end of each winding is connected to a common point, known as the **star point**. The other end of the winding is brought out to form the **phase conductor**. Each of the phase conductors is marked, as line 1, line 2 or line 3. These are colour-coded red, yellow and blue, with the neutral line being black. The neutral conductor carries no current.

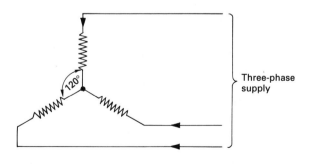

Figure 6.6   Star connection

A three-phase, four-wire system has the advantage that two different voltages are available from one supply source. Large electrical motors are connected to the three-phase supply conductors, operating at a voltage of 415 V. Small motors, socket outlets, and lighting fittings are connected between a single-phase conductor and the neutral line, operating at a voltage of (usually) 240 V.

The available voltages are shown in Figure 6.7. The voltages between the phases are

$$\sqrt{3} \times 240 \text{ V} = 415 \text{ V}.$$

Note that currents and voltages in different phases cannot be added directly as they are 120° out of phase, and the number 1.73 ($\sqrt{3}$) is used to relate the voltages and currents in three-phase calculations.

DISTRIBUTION OF ELECTRICITY IN BUILDINGS

Compared with heating pipework or air conditioning ductwork, electrical cables present less of a problem when fitting them into a building.

Figure 6.8 shows the armoured incoming cable, buried at a depth of 450 mm, entering the building through a large-radius service pipe. Once in the building it is connected to the area board's main fuse/fuses; it then passes to the kWh meter. All the services up to this point are the property of the regional electricity company. In a domestic situation, meter tails of 25 mm² cross-sectional area then pass to the consumer control unit (fuse box). These can provide a maximum demand of 25 kW.

Most small domestic installations have only a

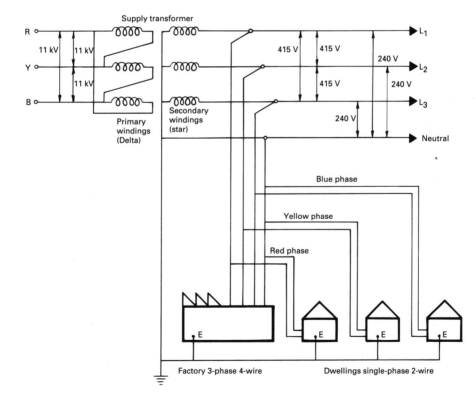

Figure 6.7 Voltages available in three-phase supply

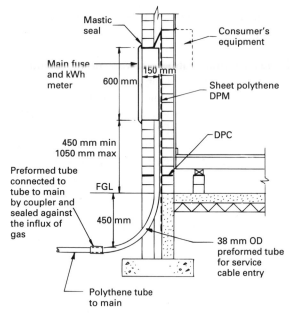

Figure 6.8 Typical domestic electrical supply

single-phase supply. However, if the maximum demand is high, consideration of a three-phase supply may be necessary.

Consumer control unit [1]

Domestic installations have a consumer control unit. These units are made in various sizes, but in general they consist of an 80 A microgap switch, with up to 12 single-phase and neutral (SPN) fuses and neutral treminals. The number of circuits provided will depend on the nature of the house/building. This unit provides a means of isolating the whole of the incoming supply and fusing all the final sub-circuits by means of rewirable fuses or miniature circuit breakers.

Fuses

A fuse is a device for opening a circuit by means of a conductor designed to melt when an excessive current flows.

The purpose of a fuse is to protect the cable and appliance from excess current flow, which may occur from a fault or result from the installation of a device

having a higher current rating than the fuse. A fuse must be capable of protecting the smallest conductor in the circuit.

The current that a given fuse element will carry continuously without deterioration is known as the **current rating**. The **fusing current** is the current at which the fuse element will melt.

Melting-wire fuses are:

- rewirable fuse [2];
- cartridge fuse [3];
- high breaking capacity [4] (HBC) fuse (formerly called high rupturing capacity (HRC) fuse).

The **rewirable fuse** is the simplest of all the fuses. It consists of a thermoplastic or porcelain bridge and base, as shown in Figure 6.9. The bridge has two sets of contacts, which fit into the base contacts. The bridge contacts have the fuse element – a tinned copper wire – connected between them.

The advantages of this type of fuse are that it is cheap to install, and it is easy to replace the fuse element. The disadvantages are that the fuse element deteriorates in use, and that the incorrect size of fuse wire can be fitted, thus defeating the purpose of the fuse.

The fuse wire has a fusing current factor of 2; this is twice the current at which the fuse will melt.

The cartridge fuse is shown in Figure 6.10, and will be recognized as the type used in a 13 A plug in the domestic ring circuit. The fuse element is

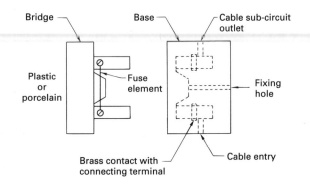

Figure 6.9 Rewirable fuse

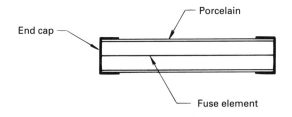

Figure 6.10 Cartridge fuse

contained in a porcelain tube fitted with two connecting caps; the fusing factor is 1.5 (50% overload). The fuses are colour coded. This fuse does not age like the rewirable fuse, but an incorrect fuse may be fitted in the plug, resulting in a system that is not correctly protected.

The **high breaking capacity fuse** is used to protect circuits against heavy overloads, opening a circuit under short-circuit conditions without damaging surrounding equipment.

Figure 6.11 shows the construction of this type of fuse. It is used in motor circuits, in which the starting current may be three times greater than the running current.

Miniature circuit breakers [5] are the ultimate protection device for consumer control units. They are available in sizes ranging from 5 A to 60 A, and they are smaller than the rewirable type. Un-

like the other fuses covered, no wire melts in these. They rely on a combination of thermal (bimetallic) and magnetic effects, to separate a pair of contacts when the current exceeds a predetermined level.

They provide close protection of the circuit, and once opened cannot be closed while a fault exists. As fuses do not have to be fitted, there is no chance of installing an oversized fuse.

Many consumer control units (ccus) are now fitted with earth leakage circuit breakers, which isolate the circuit if earth leakage currents flow.

Final subcircuits

On leaving the consumer unit/distribution board, the fused final subcircuits provide current to the various appliances. The circuits can be considered in the domestic case as consisting of lighting (ideally two circuits for houses, one circuit for small bungalows), immersion heater(s), socket outlets for kitchen/laundry area, cooker circuit, electric shower circuit, and ring main circuits for the ground and first floor. Figure 6.12 shows a typical arrangement of a domestic single-phase living system from the external mains to the consumer unit, and then to the final subcircuits.

Figure 6.13 shows a typical three-phase circuit as found in a large office block or factory. Many variations of this system are possible, depending on the diversity of services encountered in these types of building. In this case the incoming three-phase supply enters a horizontal bus bar chamber and then rises up the building, feeding distribution boards at the various levels. The circuits taken from these distribution boards may be either single- or three-phase supplies depending on requirements.

Since the Parker Morris report in 1961, **ring circuits** have become normal practice in the UK. In the domestic situation, a ring (final subcircuit) is allowed for a floor area of less than 100 m², and in this area it can have an unlimited number of socket outlets. If the floor area is greater, extra rings are required for each 100 m².

Figure 6.14 shows a ring main layout in which the live, neutral and earth conductors start at the ccu and return to the ccu, forming an unbroken loop or ring. A spur of a ring circuit is a branch cable of cross-sectional area not less than the conductors

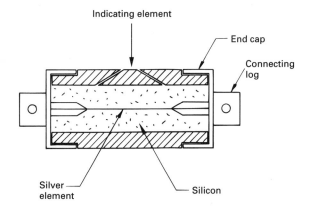

Figure 6.11 HBC fuse

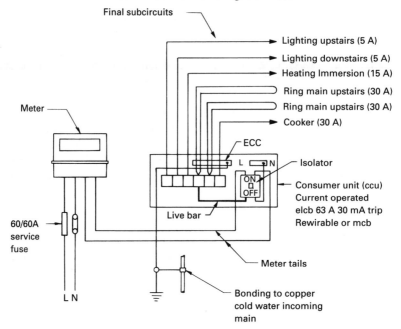

Figure 6.12 Typical domestic layout

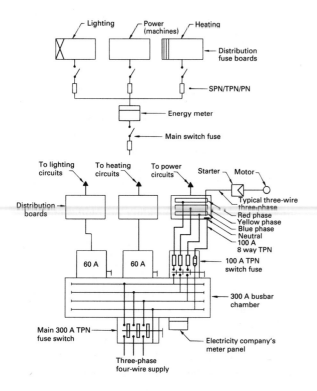

Figure 6.13 Typical factory/office distribution

forming the ring. The copper PVC insulated cables on this ring must have a minimum cross-sectional area of 2.5 mm². The socket outlets accept 13 A cartridge-fused plugs, and the cartridge fuse must be of the correct size in order to protect the circuit.

Each socket in the ring is effectively connected to the ccu, thus effectively doubling the cross-sectional area of the cable, and hence allowing a lighter cable to be used. The total loading in the circuit is calculated on the basis of a **diversity factor**, which assumes that not all appliances are in use at the same time. Before the introduction of the ring circuit, the traditional system of radial circuits was used; this had 2 A, 5 A and 15 A socket outlets all of different sizes, and was expensive to wire.

European Standards (CEN) have been considering for many years a new type of socket outlet for both domestic and commercial applications, but no decision has been made on this as yet.

For industrial and commercial applications the ring circuit is replaced by **radial circuits**. As the name suggests, these radiate out from the ccu like spokes from the hub of a wheel. This arrangement is used as the ring circuit would not be suitable;

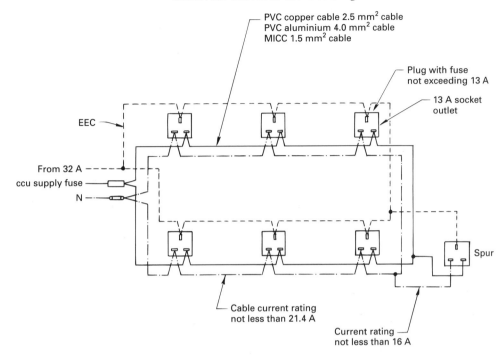

Figure 6.14 Domestic ring circuit. Maximum floor area served by each ring 100 m²; maximum length for minimum cross-sectional area 54 m

the diversity principle would result in only a limited number of sockets being allowed from each fuse.

Domestic lighting circuits are fed from a 5 A fuse; Figure 6.15 shows typical lighting circuits.

Cable types

The selection of the cable to be used depends on the prevailing environmental conditions, building construction and use.

A cable is defined as a length of insulated single conductor (solid or stranded), or of two more such conductors, each provided with its own insulation. A cable is a conductor, manufactured from a material that offers a low resistance to a flow of current. It must be mechanically strong, flexible and cheap. Silver is a better conductor than copper, but it is too expensive for practical purposes. Most conductors in common use are manufactured from copper; aluminium is used to a lesser extent. In order to make a conductor flexible, as in a kettle lead for example, many small cross-sectional area con-

ductors are stranded, with each layer of strands spiralled onto the cable in the opposite direction to the previous layer. Conductors are not always insulated; for example, bare rectangular and circular cross-section copper and aluminium conductors are used in open bus-bar systems.

In order to meet the requirements of the Institution of Electrical Engineers (IEE) Regulations, all cable sizes as given by the cross-sectional area must be capable of carrying the current for which they are designed, and the correct selection for any installation depends on:

- the current to be carried;
- the voltage drop;
- the operating temperature.

An electric current flowing through a conductor generates heat owing to the cable resistance. For a given current, the greater the conductor cross-sectional area, the less heat is generated. Excessive heat will damage the insulation.

If the temperature surrounding the cables is above or below 30 °C corrections have to be made to the current it can carry. An increase in temperature means that a cable capable of carrying a certain current at 30 °C has to be **down-rated** (to carry less current), while if the temperature is below 30 °C, it can be **up-rated** to carry more current.

If several cables are run in one conduit, duct or trunking, a temperature increase due to bunching will occur. To limit this effect the cable size may have to be increased, and the number of cables restricted to a certain percentage of the cross-sectional area of the conduit.

Owing to cable resistance, a voltage drop occurs in a cable. The IEE Regulations state that the voltage drop in a cable from the point of supply to use must not exceed 2.5 per cent of the nominal voltage (6.0 V in a 240 V supply). If the drop is greater than this, a larger-sized cable must be used.

An **insulator** is a material that offers a high resistance to the flow of electricity in all directions. It must also have the correct mechanical and chemical properties for the environment in which it is to be used. Many different types of cable insulation are in use, but at this stage only two will be considered: PVC cable and mineral-insulated cable.

Polyvinyl chloride (PVC) cable, which is thermoplastic-insulated, is widely used for domestic and commercial applications. PVC is largely unaffected by oil and many chemicals; it is non-hygroscopic, tough, durable and chemically inert, and will not support combustion.

The outer PVC sheath, as well as being the insulation, also acts as the mechanical protection. Extra protection may be provided by conduit or trunking (see below).

The cables supplying a building are called **service cables**; they may be single- or three-phase.

Cables must conform to BS 6004 : 1991 [6] and BS 6500 : 1990 [7] with subsequent amendments and CENLEC requirements. These cables are only suitable for use in temperatures above 0 °C and below 70 °C. They may have an armoured metal covering to reduce the possibility of mechanical damage.

Mineral insulated cable is often referred to as **MICC** [8] (mineral insulated copper covered). The cable consists of three parts:

- solid copper conductors;
- magnesium oxide (magnesia) insulation between the cores, capable of withstanding high temperatures;
- an outer sheath of seamless copper tube, which may be protected by an outer PVC sheath.

The cable is formed by drawing a solid section of copper or aluminium through a series of dies. The relative distance between the cores and the sheath is constant during its manufacture and its use. The space between the outer sheath and the conductors is filled with compressed magnesium oxide.

This type of cable is capable of withstanding temperatures of up to 250 °C. The outer copper sheath provides the earth continuity conductor. Unlike PVC, this type of cable does not deteriorate with age, and the diameter for a given current rating is less than that of a PVC cable.

The disadvantages are that it is expensive, and it takes a long time to make the terminations, which use a compression nut similar to those used on water systems. It is essential to ensure that moisture does not reach the insulation, which is hygroscopic: hence a special compound has to be used to stop this from happening.

Regardless of the cable used, supports at set intervals are required in order to reduce the stresses. The regulations give the support distances for different cable types.

In many cases, cables are supported in conduits, trays or trunking. This arrangement provides protection against mechanical damage, as well as providing in the case of metal an earth return path.

Conduit systems

Apart from cables running under floorboards in houses, in all other instances cables are fitted into either metallic or plastic conduit. The conduit is the mechanical protection for the cables, protecting them from damage, and the metallic conduit acts as the earth continuity conductor. It is essential not to fill the conduits with cables to more than 40 per cent of their cross-sectional area, otherwise overheating of the cables will occur. All conduits are to be supported at distances not greater than those given in the IEE Regulations.

When the number of cables to be carried becomes large, the conduit is replaced by trays or trunking (see Figure 6.15). The trunking is manufactured from mild steel sheeting or plastic, and may be either surface-mounted or buried. When various power supplies, telephone cables or computer cables follow the same path these can be carried in the same trunking, provided that they are segregated in separate compartments.

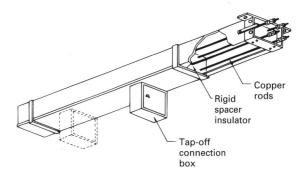

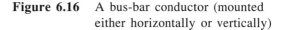

Figure 6.16 A bus-bar conductor (mounted either horizontally or vertically)

vised to pay attention to the layout of the electrical systems that are seen in everyday life.

Earthing

The subject of earthing systems is complex, and must be carried out according to the IEE Regulations.

The purpose of earthing is to connect all metalwork, apart from the conductors, to earth. With this arrangement, dangerous potential differences cannot exist, either between adjacent metallic objects, or between metallic parts and earth. Should a fault condition arise, the fault current will flow to earth through the least resistance, rather than through a person in contact with the fault.

Lighting systems

The design of lighting systems for buildings is outside the scope of this book. It will however be useful to outline briefly a few factors relating to lighting systems.

The design of interior and exterior lighting systems is carried out to the requirements of the various codes produced by the Chartered Institution of Building Services Engineers. These are based on the former Illuminating Engineering Society codes, and cover all aspects of design. The heat output of a light fitting is of prime importance on two counts:

- heat gains, which will influence the air conditioning load;
- the energy consumed by the fittings.

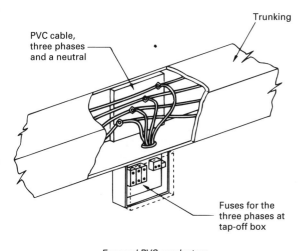

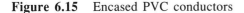

Encased PVC conductors

Figure 6.15 Encased PVC conductors

Bus-bar trunking [9]

In this arrangement copper or aluminium sections are supplied fitted in trunking or trays. The conductors are insulated only on the trunking. They are used for rising mains in tall buildings, supplying the mains to each floor; fire barriers and provision for thermal expansion must be provided. They are also used horizontally in workshops for direct connections for machines, providing flexibility for machine repositioning. Bus-bar systems must not be installed if inflammable vapours are present. Figure 6.16 shows a typical bus-bar system.

The fittings and equipment used in electrical distribution system are many and complex, and are outside the scope of this book. The reader is ad-

Lighting is required in buildings for functional, decorative and safety reasons. All these factors will influence the actual power requirements and the resulting cable size.

Much has changed in light bulb production since the first practical incandescent carbon filament lamp was demonstrated by Joseph Swan in 1879. Today the nearest lamp to the one developed by Swan is the tungsten filament (GLS) lamp. In this, a tungsten filament is heated to incandescence, contained in a bulb filled with an inert gas; it has an operating life of about 1000 hours, with a poor efficacy in the 8–18 lumens/watt range. (The lumen (lm) is the SI unit of luminous flux. It is used to define the total light omitted by a source or received by a surface. Hence the efficiency of different fittings can be compared by knowing the number of lumens produced per watt of input power.)

A tubular fluorescent lamp, in contrast, has a life of around 10 000 hours with an efficacy in the 37 100 lumens/watt range. The above two are typical of domestic and some forms of commercial lighting. In industrial applications, many other types of lamp can be found; typical examples are the high-pressure mercury lamp, having a life of about 20 000 hours, and an efficacy in the 35 lumens/watt range, and the low-pressure sodium lamp (SOX) which has an efficacy of up to 190 lumens/watt.

Light fittings, as well as switches, are earthed for safety. Special fittings are required in wet areas or in factories where explosive gases or dusts are present. Typical cable layouts are as those shown in Figure 6.17.

ELECTRICAL REGULATIONS

The purpose of the various electrical regulations is to ensure a safe electrical system by eliminating the following:

- excess current;
- electric shock;
- corrosion;
- fire;
- explosion;
- leakage;
- mechanical damage.

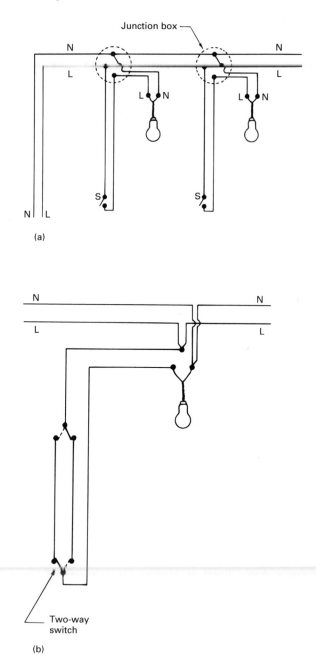

Figure 6.17   Typical wiring for lights: (a) the tap-in or jointing method for a lighting circuit; (b) two-way switching for lights

The main regulations are

- the Electricity Acts;
- the Electricity at Work Regulations 1989;
- the IEE Regulations (BS 7671 : 1992);
- the Comité Européen de Normalisation Electrotechnique (CENELEC, the European Committee for Electrotechnical Standardization), and other international regulations.

The Electricity Acts and Electrical Supply Regulations 1937

These place an obligation on the regional electricity company to supply electricity to everyone in their area who asks for it. The cost of this supply will depend on the work involved in supplying or extending the existing network. This Act also gives certain government departments the power to make further regulations to control the supply of electricity.

The regulations also give the regional companies certain powers of supervision over the consumer's installation, and the power to withhold or disconnect a supply. Their purpose is to ensure the safety of the public and to safeguard a proper and sufficient supply of electricity. Under these regulations, the area board undertakes to supply the consumer at a stated voltage phase and frequency, with permitted variations. These regulations have the force of law, and legal action can be taken against anyone who disregards them.

In practice, however, problems seldom arise, as the installer will carry out work to these regulations, with a certificate of completion showing verification of polarity, insulation tests and earthing tests.

The Electricity at Work Regulations 1989

These came into force on 1 April 1990, and replaced the 1908 and 1944 Electricity (Factories Act) Special Regulations. They are made under the Health and Safety at Work Act 1974 (HSWA).

However, unlike the regulations that they replaced, they apply to all places of work, including shops, offices, educational establishments, private institutions, and public buildings, as well as factories.

The regulations are contained within one 16-page document, which is divided into four parts:

- Part I: Regulations 1 to 3, interpretation of terms used and persons on whom duties are imposed.
- Part II: Regulations 4 to 16. This is the main technical substantive provision relating to industry in general.
- Part III: Regulations 17 to 28, applying to mines.
- Part IV: Regulations 29 to 33. These are the miscellaneous requirements covering the defence regulations, exemption certificates, disapplication of duties, and revocations and modifications to existing regulations.

The purpose of the regulations is to prevent injury to any person from electrical causes in connection with work activities. Ignorance of the law is no defence. A Magistrates' Court can impose a £2000 fine, while a Crown Court can give an unlimited fine and up to 2 years' imprisonment for non-observance of the regulations.

Institution of Electrical Engineers Regulations 16th Edition 1991 (IEE Wiring Regulations)

Buildings completed after December 1992 must comply with the 16th Edition. Unlike the previous two sets of regulations, there are no legal requirements for the IEE Regulations. In general, however, if the IEE Regulations are met, the requirements of the other two regulations will be satisfied.

The regulations are drawn up by the Wiring Committee of the IEE, and consist of:

- Part 1: Scope, object and fundamental requirements for safety (Chapters 11, 12 and 13).
- Part 2: Definitions of terms.
- Part 3: Assessment of general characteristics (Chapters 31–34).
- Part 4: Protection for safety (Chapters 41–47).
- Part 5: Selection and erection of equipment (Chapters 51–56).
- Part 6: Special installations or locations.
- Part 7: Inspection and testing. (Chapters 71–74).

These are followed by six appendices. Construction sites have many dangerous areas: for example, electricity in wet and confined spaces, steelwork dropped on unprotected electrical cables, jib cranes coming into contact with overhead cables, or underground cables being dug up. Hence it is important that full compliance with the regulations is observed in order to ensure electrical safety.

The IEE regulations are now incorporated in BS 7671 : 1992 *Requirements for electrical systems*.

International standards

The final regulations to be considered are the international standards. In the coming years, with the changes in Europe, these will gain more importance.

They are normally abbreviated as:

- IEC: International Electrotechnical Commission.
- CENELEC: European Committee for Electrotechnical Standardization.
- CEE: International Commission on Rules for the Approval of Electrical Equipment.

At this stage no attempt will be made to delve into these, but the reader should be aware that they exist and refer to them when updating specifications.

QUESTIONS

1 With the aid of neat annotated sketches explain how electricity is generated in a fossil fuel power station and distributed to consumers.
2 Describe how a single-phase 240 V supply is obtained from a 415 V distribution network.
3 Why is it necessary to step up the voltage at a power station, and step down as the distribution mains enter towns? How is this step-up and step-down process achieved?
4 By the aid of neat annotated sketches describe three types of fuse, stating the application and the advantages and disadvantages of each type.

5 Show by means of a sketch how a three-phase electricity supply enters, and is distributed through, a building. Also, show how single-phase circuits are provided from a three-phase riser.
6 In the drawing-up of a contract for an electrical system discuss what regulations you would specify to ensure that the system is correctly installed.
7 Describe at least **four** different types of wiring systems that are found in buildings. (This question will require further reading of electrical installation textbooks.)
8 Discuss the purpose of the following.
   (a) conduits;
   (b) trunking;
   (c) trays;
   (d) earth wires.
   (Again, further reading will be required.)
9 What size of fuse is required on a 240 V supply if the power consumed is 1000 W?

REFERENCES

1 BS 5486 : Part 13 : 1989 *Specification for particular requirements of consumer units*
2 BS 3036 : 1992 *Specification for semi-enclosed electric fuses*
3 BS 1361 : 1986 and BS 1362 : 1986 *Specification for general purpose fuse links and cartridge fuses*
4 BS 88 : six parts (various dates) *Cartridge fuses and HBC*
5 BS 3871 : Part 1 : 1984 *Miniature air circuit breakers*
6 BS 6231 : 1990 and BS 6346 : 1989 *Specification for PVC cables*
7 BS 6500 : 1990 *Specification for insulated flexible cords and cables*
8 BS 6207 : 1991 *Specification for MICC cables*
9 BS 5486 : Part 2 : 1988 *Particular requirements for bus bar trunking requirements*

7 GAS INSTALLATIONS

INTRODUCTION

The term **gaseous fuel burner** denotes that either natural gas or liquid petroleum gases (LPG) may be burnt.

Before 1970, when natural gas became fully available in the UK, town gas was used. This is only available today from coke producers, such as steelworks. It was manufactured from the carbonization of coal in gasworks. It had a calorific value of about 18.6 MJ/m³ and contained sulphur and carbon monoxide. Natural gas, as the name suggests, is the natural product of oil wells, as in the North Sea and the Morecambe Bay gasfields. This gas is mostly methane, and has a calorific value of around 38.9 MJ/m³. Landfill sites and sewage treatment works are also a source for this type of gas.

In the past, gas was measured by a unit known as the therm, which was 100 000 British thermal units (BTU). As natural gas has a calorific value of about 1000 Btu/ft³ this means that 100 ft³ are equivalent to 1 therm. As from 1 April 1992, to meet European harmonization, the units of measurement were changed from therms to metric units: the calorific value is measured in MJ/m³, and the charges in pence/kWh.

Liquid petroleum gas is produced during the refining of crude petroleum oils. It is supplied in liquid form under pressure in cylinders or tanks to remote areas where the mains gas supply is not available. These gases are commercial butane or propane, and unlike natural gas.

Before a gas can be burnt it has to be mixed with combustion air; if the air/gas mixture is below or above a certain value combustion will not occur.

Safety in the use of gas appliances is controlled by the Gas Safety (Installations and Use) Regulations 1994 [1] and the 1995 Building Regulations [2]. In 1968 the Ronan Point disaster occurred, in which a gas explosion in a multi-storey block of flats caused extensive building damage. This episode led to more stringent regulations being introduced in the the construction of such buildings, and in the gas regulations.

Figure 7.1 shows the distribution of gas from the wellhead. The source pressure at the wellhead is in excess of 10 MPa; this is fed into a terminal station near the coast, where the pressure is reduced to about 7 MPa, allowing the gas to be conveyed in the national transmission system. At this stage, some of the gas is compressed, changing it into a liquid. This process causes a reduction in volume, which allows the gas to be readily stored, in order to provide for peak demands.

From the national transmission system, a further pressure reduction to 3.5 MPa takes place, the gas then being fed into the regional transmission system.

On leaving the regional transmission system the gas is fed into the regional distribution system; the pressures at this stage are reduced to about 700 kPa.

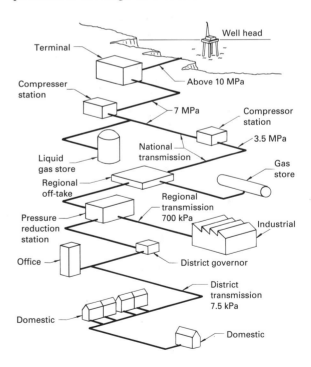

Figure 7.1 Gas distribution

Industrial users require gas at this pressure, while small commercial and domestic users have gas supplied at below 7.5 kPa.

CONNECTION OF THE GAS SUPPLY

The entry of the gas service pipe into a low-rise building may be achieved by one of the following methods:

- service entry below ground;
- service entry above ground;
- service entry below the floor;
- service entry via an external meter box;
- service entry into a garage (no more than 2 m of pipe to be exposed before connecting to the meter).

Figures 7.2 and 7.3 illustrate some of these possibilities. A minimum cover of 375 mm from the ground to the pipe is required.

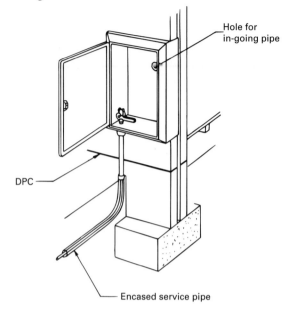

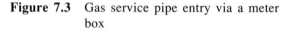

Figure 7.3   Gas service pipe entry via a meter box

If the gas supply is to be taken through to different levels of a multi-storey building, it has to be via a protected, ventilated shaft as used in Figure 7.4.

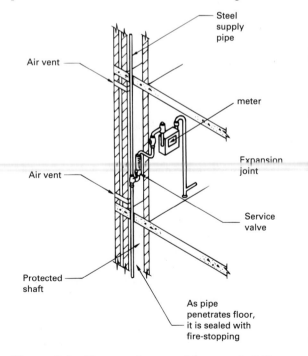

Figure 7.4   Gas supply to multi-storey building

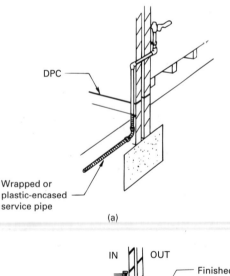

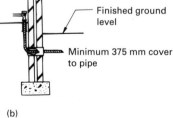

Figure 7.2   Gas service pipe entry (a) above and (b) below ground

The gas pipe supplying the meter has an isolating cock for safety purposes. The meter has a governor to control the pressure of the gas supplying the equipment. The physical size of the meter depends on the gas consumption. A typical domestic meter arrangement is shown in Figure 7.5.

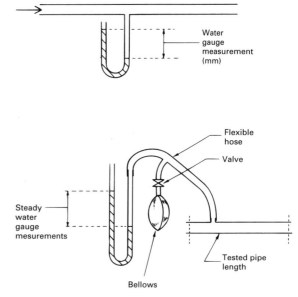

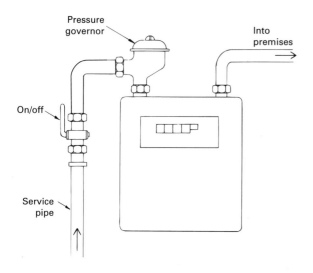

Figure 7.5   Gas meter with pressure
governor

The supply pipes can be made of copper, plastic, wrapped steel or plastic-encased steel. Where pipework passes through structural elements such as walls and floors it must be contained in a fire-stopped pipe sleeve in order to provide the necessary fire compartmentation.

After the installation of the gas pipe, a pressure test is carried out to ensure that the pipework is free from leaks. This can be achieved by pumping air into the pipe to a pressure of, say, twice its normal working pressure. The pressure is recorded by a U-tube gauge, as shown in Figure 7.6. The test pressure is held for a given time, and any drop in the pressure indicates a leak, which must be corrected before gas is allowed into the system. It is essential to determine the gas pressure at the appliance; if the pressure is not correct for the appliance, operating problems will be experienced.

Figure 7.6   Water gauge tests for gas piping

BURNER TYPES

Having supplied the gas to the appliance, the next stage is to burn it. Unlike liquid and solid fuels, if gas is provided in the correct proportions with air, it is easy to burn; the combustion process is achieved by the use of various types of burner.

Low-pressure burners of the multi-jet pattern are used for low-capacity installations, such as domestic systems; they operate on gas supply pressures in the 2.5–10 mbar pressure range. (The gas industry uses the bar as the measurement of pressure. To convert bars to Pa, multiply by 1×10^5.) The combustion air may be induced by the gas pressure, in what is known as an **atmospheric burners**; a second type is the **fan-induced burner**.

High-pressure burners are used in commercial installations, and operate in the 12–175 mbar range. Another type of burner that is found on larger installations is the **dual gas/oil burner**. This system is used to ensure that a constant supply of fuel is available; should the gas supply be lost, the oil burner comes into operation.

It is essential that the pressure of a gaseous fuel

is adjusted and controlled to suit the burner. This is achieved by the use of gas governors on both the pilot and main supply. Adequate safety devices are built into gas burners to ensure that ignition will not take place without the purging of the boiler of any build-up of gas. These flame failure devices may be either the bi-metallic or the magnetic type.

The **bi-metallic** type has a metal strip, consisting of a layer of steel alloy and brass, located in a position touching the flame of the pilot light. Owing to the different coefficients of thermal expansion of steel and brass this strip will bend when heated, allowing the gas valve to open. Should the pilot light flame fail, the strip will cool down, changing its shape and closing the main gas valve. The **magnetic type** or **thermocouple** has a tip near the pilot flame. The heated tip produces a current, which activates a solenoid on the gas valve, allowing gas to flow. Once the pilot light is extinguished, the current production is stopped, closing the gas valve.

The purpose of the above two devices is to provide a safe system. The ignition of the air/gas mixture may take place by either a gas pilot light or an electric spark.

Combustion air

In order to ensure complete combustion of the gas, adequate combustion air is required at the burner. Failure to achieve this will result in carbon monoxide, a very toxic gas, being formed. In round figures at least 10 m^3 of combustion air is required for every 1 m^3 of gas supplied. This requires adequate fresh air inlets at high and low level in the space where the combustion appliance is fitted. The actual sizes of these openings are obtained from BS 5440 : Part 2 *Air supply* [3, 4].

FLUES [3–6]

After the combustion air has mixed with the gas in the combustion chamber, ignition and combustion occurs, and it is then necessary to remove the products of combustion to a position outside the building, where they will not cause any problems. The resulting products of combustion are nitrogen, carbon dioxide, and water vapour.

Figure 7.7 shows the basic flue types available for gas firing. With the room-sealed or balanced-flue system the air enters directly into the combustion unit from outside the building, at the same point where the flue gases are discharged. This arrangement has the advantage that the wind pressures on both the fresh air inlet and the discharge are constant, thus ensuring stable combustion. The balanced flue may be fan assisted, allowing a greater distance from the appliance to the outside discharge. Basement boiler houses may have a fan dilution system fitted, in which case fresh air is drawn into a duct by means of a fan. This duct has the boiler flue connected into it; in a mid position at the other end of the duct is a centrifugal fan. This arrangement dilutes the products of combustion, allowing them to be discharged at low level. Other appliances obtain their combustion air from within the room in which they are located.

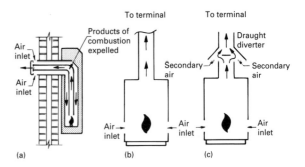

Figure 7.7 Various types of flue for gas firing: (a) room sealed (balanced flue); (b) closed flue; (c) open flue

The purpose of a gas flue is to ensure that the combustion products are discharged freely. It is essential that the flue is of the correct cross-sectional area to handle the volume of combustion products produced. With solid fuel and oil firing, the purpose of the flue is twofold: to remove the products of combustion, and to provide a draught, to aid combustion. Because of its ability to mix with air freely, gas provides its own draught.

The open flue has a draught diverter fitted, the purpose of which is to ensure that wind-produced down-draughts do not blow the products of combustion back into the boiler house.

The secondary air is that induced into the flue by the rising combustion gases. Primary air is air introduced into the combustion chamber, to mix with the neat gas.

Flue discharge

The discharge from the appliance may take place through:

- a stainless steel flue;
- a concrete flue block;
- a conventional brick chimney;
- a communal flue.

The stainless steel flue may have either a single skin or a double skin, with thermal insulation between the inside and outside diameters. The insulation is required to reduce the possibility of condensation of the flue gases taking place within the flue.

Interlocking flue blocks are used in many housing applications. The arrangement of these is shown in Figure 7.8. If a conventional brick chimney is used, a flexible flue lining has to be installed, to ensure that condensation is kept to a minimum and that falling bricks in old chimneys do not block the flue.

In multi-storey construction, room-sealed appliances may be connected to a U-duct, an SE-duct system, or the shunt duct; these communal flues are shown in Figures 7.9–7.11.

To stop birds building nests, or rain entering, the end of a flue has a terminal. It is essential that the terminal has the same free cross-sectional area as the flue connected to it, otherwise an obstruction to the passage of flue gas will be caused. Hence an approved GCI terminal must be fitted, as shown in Figure 7.12.

The Building Regulations [5] make specific demands on the details employed where flue pipes pass through the building fabric. Gas flues cannot be used for taking the products of combustion from a solid fuel fire; because of the volume of flue gas involved, they will be undersized.

All gas fitting has to be carried out by registered fitters who are members of the Confederation of Registered Gas Installers (CORGI).

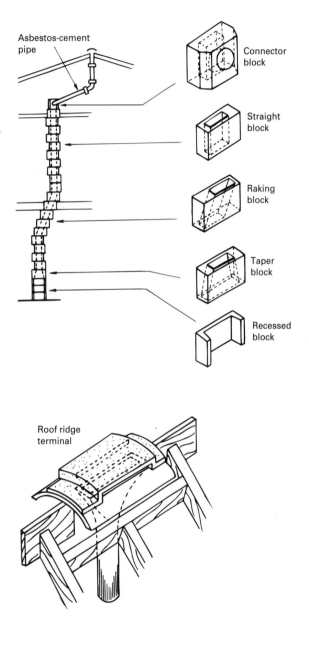

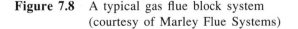

Figure 7.8 A typical gas flue block system (courtesy of Marley Flue Systems)

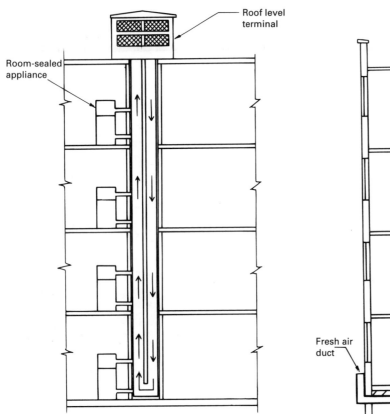

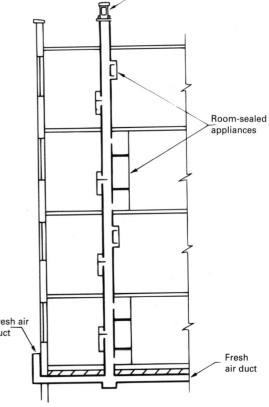

Figure 7.9   The U-duct principle

Figure 7.10   The SE-duct flue

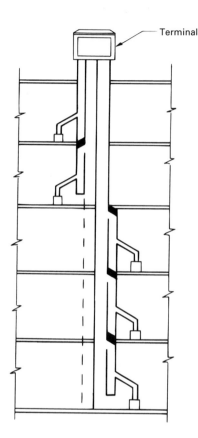

Figure 7.11 The shunt-duct flue arrangement

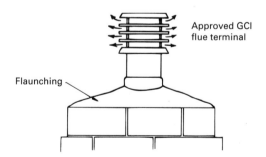

Figure 7.12 Discharge from open fire flue: terminal details

QUESTIONS

1 State the operating pressures for the following gas mains:
   (a) national transmission;
   (b) regional transmission;
   (c) district transmission;
   (d) domestic mains.

2 Discuss why it is possible to obtain methane from a landfill site. How can this gas be used?

3 Using neat annotated sketches, show all the relevant features of a gas main entering a house from the road.

4 Carry out research on what effect the Ronan Point disaster had on the supply of gas to buildings.

5 What is the purpose of a governor connected to the gas meter?

6 Discuss the factors that have to be considered in providing combustion air for a gas-fired combustion system.

7 With the aid of neat annotated sketches, show six types of flue that are used with gas-fired systems.

8 Discuss the units in which gas is sold and measured.

REFERENCES

1 The Gas Safety (Installations and use) Regulations 1994. Statutory Instrument Health and Safety 1994 No. 1886.

2 Building Regulations 1995 (effective 1 July 1995).

3 BS 5440 *Installation of flues and ventilation for gas appliances of rated input not exceeding 60 kW (1st, 2nd and 3rd family gases)* Part 1 : 1990 *Installation of flues*; Part 2 : 1989 *Installation of ventilation*

4 British Gas, *Gas in housing, a technical guide* (1990) (Covers flues and ventilation.)

5 Building Regulations 1991, J 2 *Discharge of the products of combustion*; J 3 *Protection of building*; Approved Document J, Section 2

6 BS 715 : 1989 *Sheet metal flue pipes and accessories for gas appliances*

8 SERVICES ACCESS, LIFTS AND ESCALATORS, FIRE-FIGHTING EQUIPMENT, EXTERNAL ACCESS TO BUILDINGS, SERVICES COSTS

INTRODUCTION TO SERVICE INTEGRATION

The function of a building is the usual key to the amount of electrical, mechanical, and sanitary services required: contrast the needs of, say, a hospital with a dwelling. For the dwelling, the proportion of overall construction cost attributable to the installation of services will be much smaller than far of the hospital, which could amount to as much as 50–60 per cent.

If there are extensive services to be accommodated then the routeways for installation and distribution may be so influential as to affect the basic design of the building. If, for example, the main lateral distribution route in an office block is a suspended ceiling void, this could affect the overall height of the building needed. Construction costs in this instance must not only be considered for the installation of the suspended ceilings themselves, but also for the extra external wall, windows, finishes and decoration that will be needed as a result of the extra height of the building.

When services-intensive buildings are required, there needs to be close liaison between the designer and the services engineer in an attempt to achieve:

- easy access for installation, and minimum disruption to other building activity;
- easy access for maintenance and repair, to minimize the element of disruption to the building user while speeding access for the attendant engineer;
- isolation of services to ensure the safety of occupants and to minimize nuisance by factors such as noise during operation.

There are many different ways in which pipe, cable and box-ducted services may be routed around the building, although they are basically either ver-

tical or horizontal (see BS 5588 [1]). Vertical routes, which connect the various floors of a building, are often of particular concern because of the ease with which fire could spread unless checked. Horizontal routes are often the most difficult to select, maximising access to the user needs to be balanced against interruption of the room space. To achieve horizontal movements a combination of a number of methods of accommodation may be the solution.

To ease the classification of accommodation possibilities, a division may be made into structural and non-structural alternatives. Of these, the structural methods will be particularly influential in building design, as the classification represents ducts and recesses built into the fabric of the building. By contrast, non-structural methods tend to be attachments to the structure, such as raised floors, suspended ceilings and surface trunking.

STRUCTURAL ACCOMMODATION OF SERVICES

Ducts built into the fabric of the building are often classified into three types: horizontal, vertical, and lateral. The **horizontal** group may include major services ways located below ground-floor level, such as **walkways** and **crawlways** (see Figures 8.1 and 8.2).

Walkway and crawlway ducts contain the bulk of the pipe and cable services to be routed around the floor plan of the building, and may also provide the connection between various buildings on a multi-building development, such as a hospital. It is usual to have **vertical ducts** rising from these main horizontal services routes to take the services to each floor level.

Within the main duct there will be a logical arrangement of the items conveyed. Hot pipes, for example, will be kept away from the incoming cold

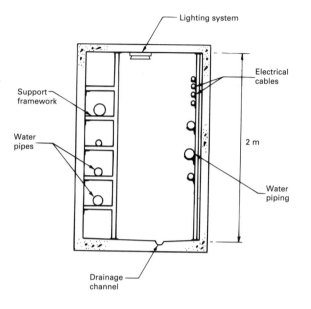

Figure 8.1 labels: Lighting system, Electrical cables, 2 m, Water piping, Support framework, Water pipes, Drainage channel

Figure 8.1 The walkway duct

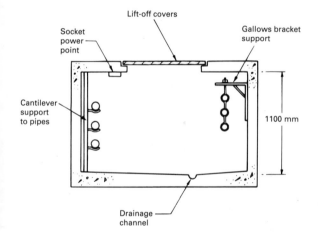

Figure 8.2 labels: Lift-off covers, Socket power point, Gallows bracket support, Cantilever support to pipes, 1100 mm, Drainage channel

Figure 8.2 The crawlway duct

the walkway, entry access may be fairly infrequent, while continuous lift-off access covers may be a feature of the crawlway to allow for the greater restrictions on movement.

Vertical ducts connecting the various floor levels in the building may be of two types: internal access vertical ducts or external access vertical ducts (Figure 8.3).

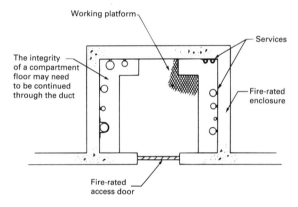

Internal access vertical duct labels: Working platform, Services, The integrity of a compartment floor may need to be continued through the duct, Fire-rated enclosure, Fire-rated access door

Internal access vertical duct

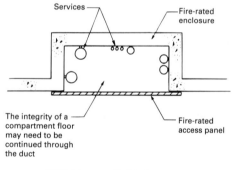

External access vertical duct labels: Services, Fire-rated enclosure, The integrity of a compartment floor may need to be continued through the duct, Fire-rated access panel

External access vertical duct

Figure 8.3 Internal and external access vertical ducts

water supplies, and water-carrying pipes will not be located above electrical cabling.

Walkways will have their own lighting system and power points at regular intervals for the connection of power tools, which may be used for installation or maintenance. By contrast the illumination of crawlways might be by plug-in lighting rather than by a permanent system.

As freedom of movement is easily achieved with

Internal access types are sufficiently large to be able to accommodate operatives while they are installing or maintaining the services, while **external access** types have fairly full access to the face of the duct by a full-width door or removable panel. The operative in this case stands outside the duct to carry out the work.

Where a branch is required from the vertical duct to transfer the services laterally on each floor, structural methods of accommodation may again apply. **Floor trenches** are recessess in the structural floor, and are usually used for the distribution of piped services (Figure 8.4). To make these ducts less conspicuous to the building occupier, it is common to top the duct with lift-off tray covers, which may be filled with screed (cement and sand) and finished with the floor finish that is to be used in that area.

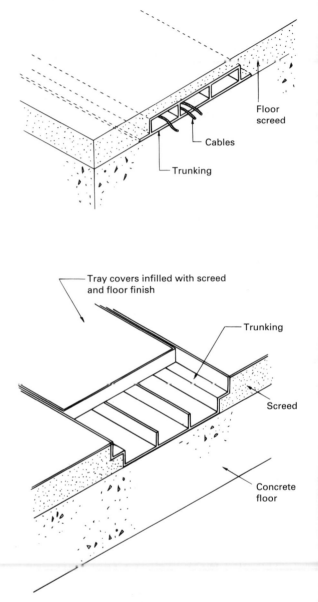

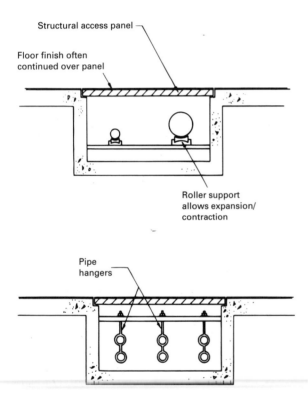

Figure 8.4 Floor trenches

Figure 8.5 Trunking embedded in the floor screed

If only cable services are to be accommodated, these may be placed in box trunking set into the floor finish. The inclusion of such details set into floor screeds is very common (Figure 8.5). Although not shown on the illustration, junction points with lift-off access covers would be provided at intersections between the trunking to allow for the formation of joints.

NON-STRUCTURAL ACCOMMODATION METHODS

Non-structural methods of accommodation for the most part are horizontal or lateral routeways for services distribution. Included in this classification are suspended ceilings, raised floors and a variety of forms of trunking.

Suspended and false ceilings may be grouped into three main types: jointless, jointed, or open (Figure 8.6).

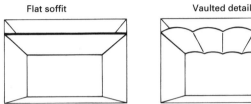

Jointless

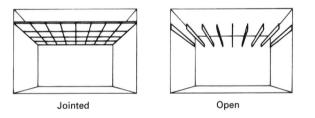

Jointed   Open

Figure 8.6   Types of suspended ceiling

Although the **jointless** class is able to take services into the ceiling void, access to the void is difficult because of the nature of the continuous ceiling finish, which is typically plaster or plasterboard. A hatch for access would need to be provided.

By contrast, the **jointed** ceiling allows full and easy access to the ceiling void, as the ceiling consists or removable tiles. The tiles are supported on a suspension framework, which is generally attached to the true structural ceiling. Figure 8.7 shows such a framework; note the use of the light-gauge pressed metal inverted 'T' members, which directly support the tiles. Around the perimeter of the room the profile of the tile support member changes to an angle section.

The ceiling void has a considerable capability to accommodate services (see Building Regulations 1991 [2]), which may include pipes, cables (generally supported on cable trays to eliminate sag), and

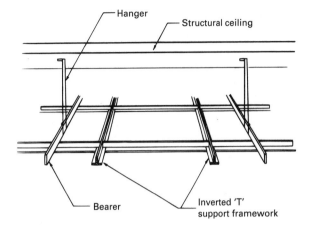

Figure 8.7   A typical support suspension framework for a suspended ceiling

air-conditioning/ventilation ducting. Many attractive types of tile are available to provide a high quality of surface finishes for the room, and these may also add significantly to the acoustic properties.

Within the jointed classification of suspended ceiling there is a further subdivision of types, which arises from the way in which the tiles are supported.

It may be that the tiles simply sit on the supporting inverted 'T' framework, which permits easy removal of the tiles but allows exposure of the supportive framework of ceiling level. Such a ceiling type is referred to an an **exposed grid system** (Figure 8.8a). Alternatively, the tiles could be fastened to the supportive framework from the underside, by screwing through the tile (using self-tapping screws – no need to drill). In this case the supportive framework is concealed, and the type classification is a **concealed grid system**, as in Figure 8.8b.

The **open** type of ceiling may or may not be a true suspended ceiling. If the boards, slats, or ornamental panels that are typically used for the ceiling finish with this arrangement are attached to the walls of the premises rather than to a framework suspended from the true ceiling, then a **false ceiling** may be a better description. Open types are used to draw the eye to the brightly coloured ceiling finish while allowing services, the upper parts of the room walls, and the true ceiling to go unnoticed. To assist in drawing the eye to the bright

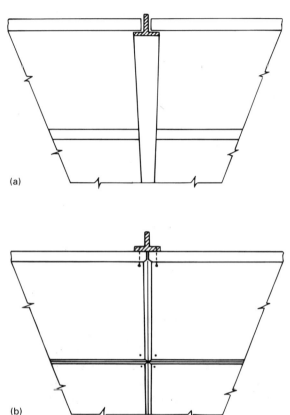

(a)

(b)

Figure 8.8 Types of jointed suspended ceiling:
(a) exposed grid system; (b)
concealed grid system

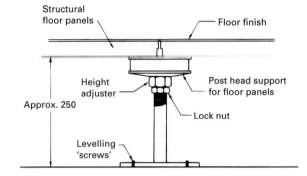

Figure 8.9 A jack post for a deep cavity raised
floor system (courtesy of Robertson
Raised Floor Systems)

ceiling finish, the area above is darkly painted.

When buildings are being refurbished this technique can also be usefully employed to reduce what would otherwise be high floor-to-ceiling dimensions.

Raised floors were originally developed for mainframe computer installations, where a 'spaghetti' arrangement of power cables was needed. They could be viewed as an upside-down suspended ceiling in that a service void is again created, this time between the true structural floor and the raised floor surface. The void was an ideal place to locate items such as power supply cables, which would otherwise present considerable nuisance to the users of the room in question.

Figure 8.9 shows a typical raised floor: this type

was a form of the original floor detail developed for computer rooms. As can be seen, there are two main components to the floor: the supportive posts and the structural floor panels. On removal of the floor panel, power cables can be draped over the jack posts, without disconnection from the machinery if necessary.

As larger-scale computers and the like are heavy items both the supportive jack post and the floor panels need to be of strong construction. Floor panels are often of composite construction, typically 600 × 600 mm in size, and are usually designed to carry loads of up to 500 kg/m^2.

In instances where it would be advantageous to have larger floor panels, an intermediate framework of beams is applied over the jack posts to support the edge of panels of up to 1200 × 1200 mm size.

Within the raised floor range a subdivision of type occurs based on the depth of the floor void. **Deep cavity** raised floors have a floor void of approximately 250 mm, whereas **shallow cavity** raised floors typically have up to 50 mm void space (Figure 8.10).

Trunking is another alternative means for the distribution of small pipes and particularly computer network cables. This is most popular in plastic or pressed metal, and can be surface mounted on both walls and ceilings. Figure 8.11 shows a typical skirting detail, which could be useful for pipe or cables where a solid floor prevents concealed distribution.

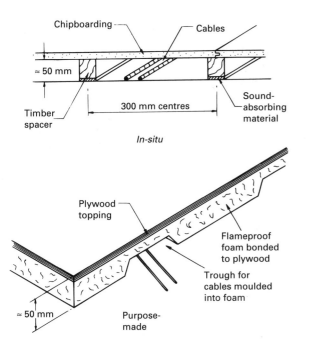

Figure 8.10 *In-situ* and purpose-made shallow cavity raised floors

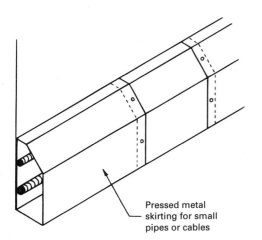

Figure 8.11 Skirting trunking of pressed metal

LIFT AND ESCALATOR INSTALLATIONS

These installations form an important and specialized aspect of building services. In order to function in an efficient manner, multi-storey buildings require correctly designed installations. The planning of such systems must commence very early in the design process to ensure that the structural and electrical aspects are met.

Use was made of hoists around 2600 BC to build the pyramids, some of which stand of over 150 m in height, and have blocks weighing 90 tonnes each.

Archimedes in 236 BC designed a pulley-operated hoist, on which the ropes were connected to a winding drum. The treadmill was another device developed at about the same time. In AD 80 the Coliseum in Rome built by the Emperor Titus had large elevators to raise the gladiators and wild animals to the level of the arena.

Animal-powered elevators were used from the early days until the introduction of the steam engine, which was used for lifting coal from mine shafts. It can be said that all the devices used up until 1852 had inherent safety problems. 1852 was the year that Otis invented the safe elevator.

Steam power for elevator use presented many problems in tall buildings. In December 1889 the first direct-connected electric elevator was installed in New York. In more recent years vast strides have been made in lift operation using electronic components.

The incorporation of vertical transport into a building must be considered at the earliest stage of the contract; failure to do this will result in a costly installation and possible structural changes. The selection of the equipment must match the requirements of the building. As is the case with other specialist services, liaison with the designer, structural, mechanical and electrical engineers is required at an early stage of the design process.

The building use, shape and height will determine the type of vertical transport to be installed. The demands placed on both the manufacturer and designer are covered in detail in BS 5655 : Part 1 : 1985 [3].

The machine room for the lift may be located at the top or at the bottom of the lift shaft, the roping arrangements being different in each case. Regardless of the position of the plant room, adequate space is required for maintenance, together with access provision to allow large items of plant to be replaced.

Figure 8.12 shows a typical shaft layout with the machine room at the top. The pit of the shaft contains buffers for the lift cage, and is tanked to ensure that water does not enter. Smoke ventilation is required, the free area for this in each shaft being not less than 0.1 m².

The standard of the building work necessary in the formulation of the shaft is critical on the following counts.

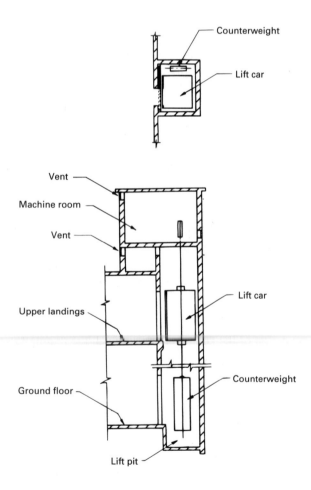

Figure 8.12　A typical lift shaft

- The lift shaft must be plumb.
- The landing entrances as they run one above the other must also be plumb.
- The plan dimensions are critical, as the car has to have the correct clearance in this opening.

The lift motor room requires a lifting beam, antivibration mountings, adequate ventilation and many other features. The involvement of the builder, services engineer and the lift manufacturer is covered in BS 5655 : Part 6 : 1985 [4].

The lift manufacturer will not start work on site until the well construction and machine room are complete, to ensure that clear access and dry and dust-free conditions exist.

Good service from lifts depends on a number of factors:

- the building's use;
- the number of floors to be served;
- the total distance of travel;
- the total number of people or weight of goods to be carried;
- peak-time concentrations of use;
- the lift speed (including the vertical speed, as well as the opening and closing times of the doors and call time, and loading and unloading times);
- lift bank position in building (an arrangement of more than one lift is known as a lift bank).

The lift shafts are normally positioned near the main entrance of the building, with a minimum service standard of one lift for every four floors. A maximum walking distance from the lift lobby to the work place is 45 m. It is of interest to note that in Japan lifts are not provided in general buildings unless they are over four floors.

In large buildings there is the problem of balancing the economic benefits of grouping the lift shafts together with the passenger congestion that this causes.

The operating speed of a lift varies according to its application; for example, shops, offices, warehouses, etc. The speed selected will be determined not only by the efficiency of the vertical travel, but by the economy of the power consumption.

Typical car speeds for up to 4 floors are 0.75 m/s; above this height 2–3 m/s up to 15 floors, and 5–7 m/s over 15 floors.

Types of lift

Three different types of lift drive are in general use:

- traction drive;
- drum drive;
- electro-hydraulic drive.

With **traction drive**, the lift car is suspended from a set of steel wire ropes, which fit into V- or U-shaped grooves cut into a traction sheave. It is the friction between the rope and the sheave that produces the drive. The other end of the cable is attached to a counterbalance weight.

The purpose of the weight is to balance to some extent the lift car and its load, hence reducing the energy required to operate the lift car. The weight of the counterweight is normally equal to the car weight, plus half the actual load to be carried.

The traction sheave is driven by a high-speed electric motor via a worm reduction gear. Roping arrangements vary according to circumstances and may be either 1:1, 2:1 or 3:1 roping.

The machine rooms may be either directly over the lift, or at the side or the bottom of the lift well. Figure 8.13 shows a single-wrap arrangement, which is used for light loads, and a 3:1 arrangement used for heavily loaded cars.

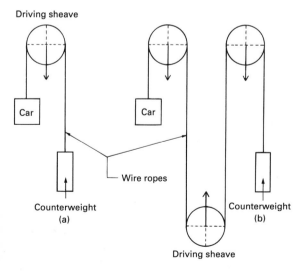

Figure 8.13 Lift roping arrangements: (a) single wrap; (b) 3:1 roping

The **drum drive** arrangement is found in short-travel applications; the suspension ropes are wound on the drum in a similar manner to a crane drive. As in the previous case the drum is driven by a high-speed electric motor through a worm reduction gear box. As no counterweight is fitted, the power consumption for operation is greater than that of the traction drive.

The **electro-hydraulic** method of drive [5] is only suitable for short- or medium-rise lifts. The lift car is connected either directly or indirectly via a rope or chain to a long-stroke hydraulic ram at the lift base. An oil pump produces, via control valves, high-pressure oil flow in or out of a hydraulic cylinder. The operation may be considered to be similar to that of a hydraulic jack used for lifting motor cars.

For certain applications this method of operation results in lower building costs. It provides a smooth operation; however, as no counterbalance weight is used, the electrical loading is greater than that required for the traction lift.

The traction lift may operate from a single-speed a.c. motor, providing a running speed in the range of 0.5 m/s, which is suitable for low-rise and light operating traffic. For lifts requiring a velocity of up to 1.0 m/s a two-speed, pole change motor is used. Above this speed, either the Ward-Leonard variable voltage principle is used, obtained from an a.c./d.c. motor generator, from a variable-speed a.c. motor, or from a gearless machine. The underlying theory relating to the above drives is beyond the scope of this book.

Safety in lift systems depends on two components, the overspeed governor and the safety breaks, both of which come into operation in the event of the speed exceeding a prescribed limit.

Lift cars

Lift cars are designed to carry set operating loads and speeds, known as the **contract load** and **contract speed**. The car is essentially a metal case secured to a structural frame. The size and the nature of the interior of these cages depends on the application (Figure 8.14).

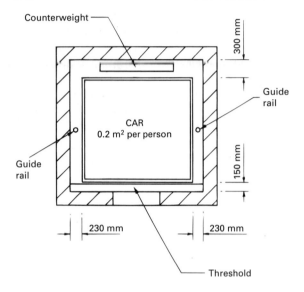

Figure 8.14 A typical lift shaft detail

Lift control systems [6]

Lift control is achieved by means of pushbuttons in the car and on the landing; a considerable degree of sophistication with these controls is possible. Briefly, the controls can be classed as:

- automatic pushbutton;
- collective;
- group control.

The **automatic pushbutton** system is used for light traffic and low-rise buildings; it can store and act on only one instruction at a time. In other words, if the lift is stationary, and a button is pressed, the lift will travel to the required floor and remain at that level for another call.

The **collective** system will receive and store calls in its memory when it is either at rest or in motion. Arrangements can be made to ensure that the lift operates in such a manner that the waiting time at any one floor is reduced to a minimum.

In the case of a tall building with three or more lifts the **group control** system is used; this makes full use of the latest micro-chip technology in order to ensure an efficient operating system.

Load cells may be used to stop lifts in tall buildings from operating at peak times until a set load is in the lift, thus ensuring economic operation.

In certain applications the control of lifts may be by an attendant. Other lift types encountered are the fireman's lift, lifts for the handicapped and the goods lift, each of these requires different operating characteristics.

Escalators

The first operative escalator was used at the Paris Exposition in 1900. Since then, escalators have been installed in situations where rapid movement of large numbers of people is needed, and applications have proved most useful in airports, underground stations and large retail stores.

Direct comparisons with lift installations are diffiicult because of the different methods of operation: escalators deal with continuous loads while batch loads are conveyed by a lift.

BS 5656 : 1983 [7] concerns the safety rules for the construction and installation of escalators and passenger conveyors. In addition to safety, other design features include:

- a high carrying capacity;
- no waiting interval;
- flexibility (since reversible);
- reliability.

Typical standard installations may carry up to 10 000 persons per hour with a conveyance speed of 0.5 m/s. Figure 8.15 shows some typical dimensions, and indicates the space necessary to accommodate the component parts. The need for clear headroom space is also featured.

The slope or pitch of the escalator is usually 30° or 35°, depending on the space available.

Reversible direction of motion provides added flexibility, which can be put to best advantage in situations such as underground stations to allow for peak flow movement preferences. The London Underground and Paris Metro both benefit from this flexibility.

When installing the escalator, the most common arrangement is the criss-cross layout as shown in Figure 8.16. The dimension *D* marked on this

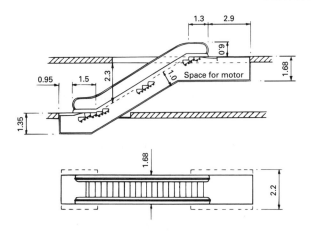

Figure 8.15 Escalators: typical installation dimensions (in metres)

illustration can be varied to suit the available space. Safety of passengers is ensured by the following:

- an emergency stop button, found at the top and bottom of the escalator by the potentially dangerous comb plates;
- a governor to regulate the speed, and specifically prevent the escalator from running too fast;
- automatic controls to bring the escalator smoothly to a halt in the event of a power or mechanical problem;
- a handrail that moves at exactly the same speed as the steps;
- balustrades, handrail and side panels that discourage the catching of clothing or packages;
- a level of illumination of at least 100 lux to the steps.

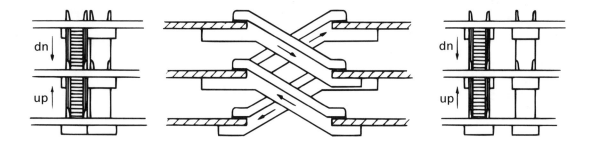

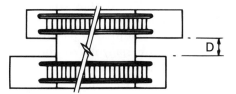

Figure 8.16 Escalators serving successive floors

Many of the buildings served by escalators are compartmentalized for the purpose of fire confinement. To preserve the integrity of such fire compartments, the escalator can be fitted with steel roller shutters, which will close off the stairway on the activation of a smoke detector, heat detector or fusible link (Figure 8.17).

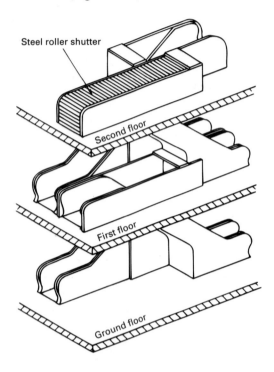

Figure 8.17 Escalators: the use of fire roller shutters

Sprinklers may provide an alternative source of fire control. These may be used in conjunction with fans, which can be utilized to pressurize the stairwell by a system of spray nozzle curtaining. Here high-pressure water nozzles create a water curtain to discourage flame and smoke movement, these being activated either by heat or smoke detectors.

In contrast to escalators, passenger conveyors have a very shallow incline, so eliminating the need for steps. The result is a continuous conveyor belt, which can carry passengers and luggage. With operation speeds at more than twice those of the escalator,

around 1–1.3 m/s, the capacity for carrying passengers is very high.

It is particularly important for the passenger conveyor to have sufficient space available at the point of termination to allow free movement for those leaving it, so minimizing congestion at this point.

FIRE-FIGHTING INSTALLATIONS

Before considering the various aspects of fire-fighting installations, it will be prudent to consider the precautions that must be taken to minimize the risks of fire hazard. These can be considered under three main headings:

- reducing the number of fire outbreaks;
- ensuring that adequate facilities are provided for escape;
- reducing fire spread within the building and to adjacent buildings.

A study of combustion chemistry shows that the following factors are involved: the flame triangle, and the 3 Ts.

The **flame triangle** consists of the following three items:

- ignition source;
- fuel;
- air (oxygen).

The removal of any one of these will ensure that combustion will not take place or will cease. Often, it is not possible to remove any of these, as in an office for example: hence the possibility of fire.

The 3 Ts are:

- time;
- temperature;
- turbulence.

In order for combustion to start and continue it is essential that the flame is at the correct temperature, there is sufficient time to ignite the materials and to have sufficient turbulence of the air or flue gases over the material.

With the above factors in mind, we can now consider the methods used to control a fire. The fire behaviour of a structure will depend on the nature of the materials used in construction. The aim of **passive control** is to reduce the use of combustible materials to a minimum.

Active control is achieved by installing equipment to fight fire outbreak. The Building Regulations [8] stipulate the fire resistance of the structural elements, so that passive control is in-built to some extent. Related to this is the division of buildings into compartments having set fire resistance of floors and walls. Where service openings for pipes and ducts, pass from one space to another, fire stopping is required to prevent direct contact of flame and smoke with adjacent areas.

Active control [9] can be achieved in many ways. The selection of the actual system depends on:

- the nature of the fire to be dealt with;
- the fire load (the combustible content per m^2 of floor area) (kJ/m^2);
- the fire classification;
- the active involvement of the occupants in extinguishing the fire;
- the ability of the occupants to leave the building unaided (this is of prime importance in relation to both the infirm and children).

Active control methods can be subdivided into **first aid measures**, involving the occupants using portable equipment to extinguish small fires, and **fixed fire-fighting appliances**.

The portable appliances [10] cover such items as fire blankets [11], water, dry powder, foam, vaporizing liquids and gases. The **water extinguisher** is the type that we are most familiar with; it is painted red, and contains 9.0 litres of water, which is expelled with pressure from a nozzle when a carbon dioxide cartridge inside the cylinder is punctured. It is for use on wood, paper and textile fires; it must *not* be used on oil or electrical fires.

The **dry powder extinguisher** is used on all fire types; it contains up to 11 kg of bicarbonate of soda, pressurized by carbon dioxide. The cylinder is coloured blue.

The **foam cylinder** is coloured cream, and is used on petroleum fires; it ranges in size from 4.5 to 45 litres. As with the other types, a pressure build-up in the cylinder expels the foam.

The vaporizing liquid extinguisher is coloured green and provides a very efficient method of producing a rapid flame knock-down. It uses halon gases, which interrupt the flame mechanism and stop the fire. These gases are now banned for environmental reasons, and this type of extinguisher is being phased out. Replacement vaporizing liquids are being introduced that do not adversely affect the ozone layer.

The **carbon dioxide extinguisher** is coloured black, and is used on electrical and liquid fires. As the vapour is heavier than air, it displaces the air around the fire, thus excluding oxygen from it.

Permanent equipment is the next to be considered. As the name suggests it consists of fixed pipes, which carry the extinguishing agents. It normally comprises:

- a sprinkler system;
- a hose reel system;
- a riser systems (these may be either dry or wet).

Sprinkler systems

These are common in many commercial and industrial buildings. Because sprinklers are so reliable, insurance companies normally reduce their premiums on buildings when sprinklers are installed. Unlike other fire-fighting systems, the sprinkler system is automatic, operating when the heat from the fire bursts a bulb, thus allowing a spray of water to fall on to the fire.

The performance of such a system is very good and normally results in containment of the fire. The sprinkler system may comprise any of the following:

- a wet system;
- a dry system;
- wet and dry systems.

The **wet system** is a water-charged network of pipes with sprinkler heads at about 3.0 m spacings; a typical arrangement is shown in Figure 8.18. The piping arrangements are complicated, requiring duplicate pumps, carefully sized break tanks and alarms. These are not shown in Figure 8.18 and

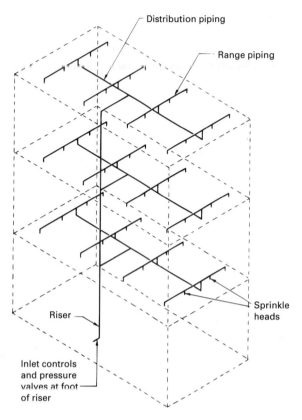

Figure 8.18   The distribution pipe network for a typical sprinkler installation

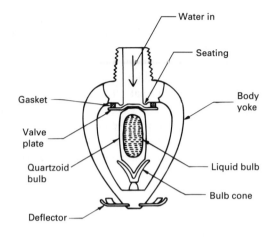

Figure 8.19   A quartzoid sprinkler head

the reader is advised to carry out some research in order to understand typical layouts.

The operating mechanisms of sprinkler heads can vary with the type, so at this stage it should be considered simply as a device, consisting of a breakable glass bulb and a spring seal, which closes the waterway. The sprinkler bulb (Figure 8.19) is selected according to the required operating temperature and spray pattern. A liquid and a small air bubble is contained in the bulb. Heat generated by the fire causes the liquid to expand, and the bubble to disappear. When this happens, pressure builds up in the bulb by expansion, causing the bulb to burst, allowing the sprinkler to open. Water then discharges freely, striking the deflector and causing a conical spray of water to spread out over the area below. The coverage depends on water pressure and sprinkler type: typical areas protected by

one head are 7.5 m² in high-risk buildings and 21 m² in low-risk buildings. High racked storage areas require special treatment.

As the system is full of water, it is not suitable for areas where freezing or high temperatures are likely, and in these cases a dry system is used.

With the **dry system** the pipework is filled with air, and when a fire breaks out the sprinkler head opens as described above, allowing the air to escape. Once a bulb bursts the reduction in air pressure operates the pump, rapidly filling the system with water.

A **wet and dry system** can be filled with water during the summer months, and air during the winter.

In certain industrial plants, some areas are protected by the **deluge system**. In this arrangement all the sprinkler heads open at the same time, either flooding the area or soaking the wall of the building, stopping the fire from reaching adjacent buildings.

Hose reel systems [12, 13]

A 25 mm diameter **hose reel system** provides a method that can rapidly be used by the staff while waiting for the fire brigade. The reels are positioned in corridors near the stairwells, the minimum water pressure at each reel is 200 kPa, and each nozzle has a minimum water flow rate of 0.4 l/s.

The reel is supplied from a pipe, of minimum diameter 50 mm, which rises up the building, either directly from the water main or from a break tank with duplicate pumps; an automatic air valve is provided at the top of this pipework.

The hose reel system must not be confused with the dry riser and wet riser systems.

Figure 8.20a shows a typical **dry riser** [14], which as the name suggests has no water in it until required. Dry risers are used in buildings up to 60 m high, and consist of a 100 mm or greater diameter pipe located in a staircase enclosure. A 65 mm double inlet breaching piece is positioned on the outside wall within a wired glass covered box. The fire brigade, on arrival, will connect this breeching piece to their engine and/or the street main.

The **wet hydrant riser** [14] is a pipe 100 mm diameter or greater that is permanently charged with water. This pipe rises up the building and has 65 mm instantaneous valved outlets on each floor for the fire brigade hose connection. The water is supplied by duplicate pumps on the outlet side of the break tank. When water flows due to valve opening, a pressure switch is activated, allowing water to be pumped into the pipework from the break tank.

Fire detection

The best fire-fighting system in the world is of little use once a fire becomes fully established: hence it is essential to have some method of detection, which will give rapid warning of a fire before it becomes established.

Manual alarms are suitable only if a building is manned and the fire is noticed in adequate time. It is essential to consider the installation of automatic detection systems to protect buildings outside working hours.

Many different detectors are available, and their selection depends upon the risk involved; these can be considered as being hazardous situations, such as encountered in the petrochemical industry, and general applications.

Typical in the general range are:

- ionization detectors (found in most buildings; a very sensitive method of fire detection);
- visible smoke detectors, which may operate via light-scattering techniques or light-obscuring techniques;

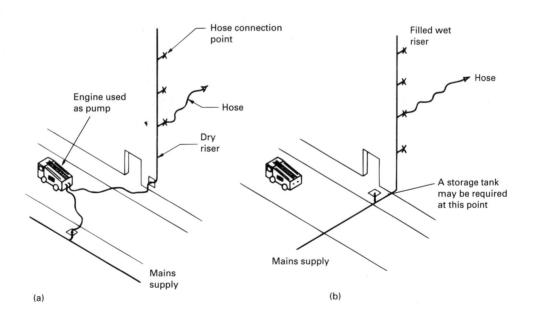

Figure 8.20 (a) Dry and (b) wet riser systems

- flame detectors, which respond to either the in-frared or ultraviolet band of the visible light spectrum;
- ultrasonic and laser detectors;
- combustion gas detectors;
- heat detectors, which include bimetallic strips, thermistors, thermocouples, fusible links, and capillary tubes.

Selection of fire-fighting systems

The selection of the fire-fighting system for a building depends on many factors. The Building Regulations help to reduce the risk of fire in building by specifying the materials to be used. It is the type and amount of combustible materials in a building that present the greatest problems.

Single-storey buildings may have roof vents that allow the smoke from a fire to escape, and by so doing allow occupants to escape without experiencing the problems of toxic smoke, or not being able to see escape routes.

The selection of systems for hospitals, old people's homes and schools will have to meet stricter requirements than, say, a sports hall. Areas in which electrical fires may be experienced would not use a conducting material such as water; in such cases CO_2 or powder would be used. Oil fires in areas such as boiler houses or kitchens require the use of foam, as flaming oils and fats would float on water. Care has to be taken with wet risers and sprinkler systems, as vandals may set them off causing a considerable amount of water damage.

Provision for fire-fighting personnel

The Building Regulations 1991 [15] include special provision for access for fire-fighters to be included in certain buildings as part of the building design.

Protected shafts containing stairways and even lifts for the sole use of fire-fighters are now needed in in many tall or large buildings. These buildings include

- any building with a floor 20 m or more above ground level;
- any building with a basement 10 m or more below ground level;
- any building with a floor of 600 m² or more,

which is 7.5 m or more above ground level;
- any building with two basement storeys where the storeys are over 900 m²

The protected shaft is a fire-rated enclosure inside which the fire-fighting personnel can move in safety through the various levels of the building. An intervening lobby is to be included in the design (Figure 8.21), where hoses may be connected before entering the floor required. Shaft ventilation is to be provided in accordance with BS 5588 [16].

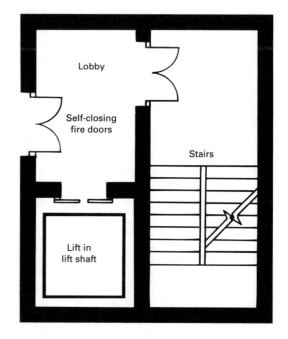

Figure 8.21   Access shaft for fire-fighting personnel

Lifts as part of this provision are required only where buildings have a floor more than 20 m above ground level, or a basement 10 m or more below ground level.

ACCESS FOR EXTERIOR MAINTENANCE

The extent of maintenance necessary to the exterior fabric of the building will depend on a number of factors:

- the geometry of the building design (plan shape and height);
- the quality, nature, and arrangement of the exterior materials;
- the degree of exposure of the building to the weather;
- the availability of finance to pay for the work.

When considering the ease with which access could take place, the plan shape of the building is often a good indicator. Simple shapes generally facilitate reasonable access. Additionally, plan shape is also a good indicator of the physical area of the fabric in question. The schedule contained in Figure 8.22 shows that a simple square shape will maximize the enclosure space for the least wall perimeter. A good indicator of the efficiency of space enclosure is given by the wall-to-floor ratio; the smaller the result the more efficient the shape (Figure 8.22).

In terms of the expense of building services provision, building shape efficiency may influence not only initial cost but also the running costs incurred over the life of the building. Efficient floor enclosure shapes lead also to efficient internal air volumes, and this may be directly linked to expenditure, for example, on mechanical ventilation or air conditioning.

If the three shapes in Figure 8.22 are examined with a view to making statements related to initial building costs, clearly A will involve the least expenditure if the same specification of materials is used on all three shapes.

Many materials used on the exterior fabric of the building will be carefully examined in terms of performance, as they will have to resist the external environmental conditions and exposures, dependent on the location and orientation of the building. Choices will have to be made in relation to the expense of materials from an initial cost point of view and also in terms of their maintenance needs. For some items such as glass, the long-term maintenance costs are usually noteworthy. It may be the case that the best materials will be placed on the elevation that, owing to the orientation of the building, will take the worst weather.

The nature of the materials of the fabric of the building will to an extent also influence the proposed means for gaining access for cleaning and maintenance purposes. The associated equipment for gaining access may be permanently attached to the building or may be brought to site on a temporary basis. Permanent equipment tends to be linked with high initial costs but efficient and low attendant costs. For portable temporary equipment the attendant costs are generally higher, owing to the increased time element.

External access equipment

The equipment allowing external access to the face of the building will involve access gained from either ground level or roof level. Different forms of equipment will vary considerably in cost and also in the speed of coverage that their deployment allows.

A division can be made into temporary and permanent equipment. **Temporary equipment** may include:

- ladders;
- stagings;

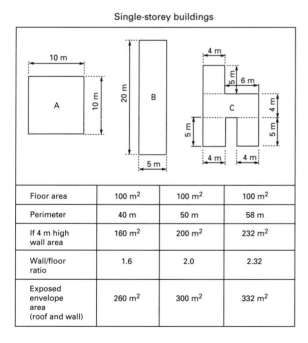

Single-storey buildings

Floor area	100 m²	100 m²	100 m²
Perimeter	40 m	50 m	58 m
If 4 m high wall area	160 m²	200 m²	232 m²
Wall/floor ratio	1.6	2.0	2.32
Exposed envelope area (roof and wall)	260 m²	300 m²	332 m²

Figure 8.22 The influence of design shape on perimeter and wall area

- single-operative systems;
- adjustable platforms;
- temporary cradles.

Ladders obviously have limited reach, and provide slow movements of the attendant operative, but they can be used from projecting building features such as balconies. The term **staging** applies to various forms of temporary scaffold-like towers, as outlined in BS 1139 [17]. These, like ladders, have a limited reach capability. Some typical details are shown in Figure 8.23.

Small amounts of maintenance and repair may be undertaken by using **single-operative** access systems, which can be lowered over the side of the building. Vertical movements with such systems are reasonable, but horizontal movements will mean dismounting and repositioning the temporary suspension arm. A cantilevered assembly could be the method of support for this system, as used for the cradle in Figure 8.24.

Adjustable platforms come in two main forms, those that operate concertina fashion while maintaining the platform in a horizontal position, and those that are vehicle mounted, and are often used for street light maintenance.

As shown in Figure 8.24, cradles can be temporarily lowered from the roof of the building using a cantilever system, but they may also be attached to supportive structures, which form permanent anchorages located at roof level (Figure 8.25).

To increase the efficiency of movement a similar suspension frame for cradle attachment may be movable by pushing manually on a trackway on the roof. Provided that an operative is based at roof level at the appropriate time, rapid horizontal movement can be made in addition to raising and lowering the cradle (Figure 8.26).

Permanent equipment may include travelling ladders, and powered trolleys with cradles.

The **travelling ladder** system has an alloy ladder permanently mounted across a glazed area to allow access for cleaning and repair. It would be normal for the operative to access the ladder by climbing through a window to the premises and attaching a safety line. Once on the ladder, horizontal movements are achieved by the operative pulling themselves along.

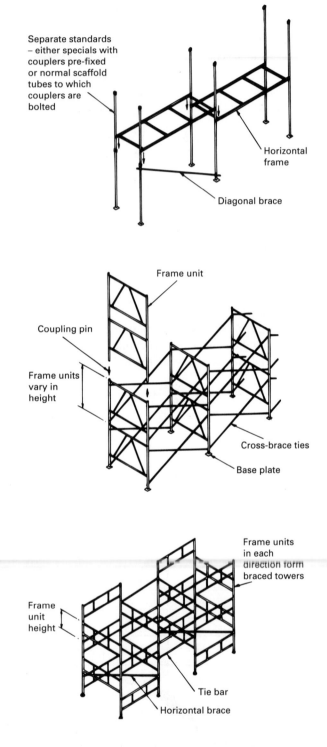

Figure 8.23   Access towers for maintenance

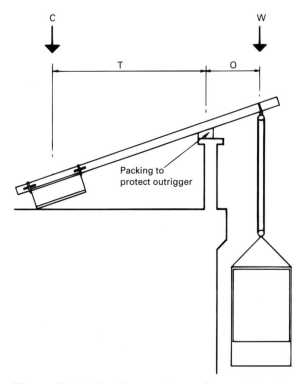

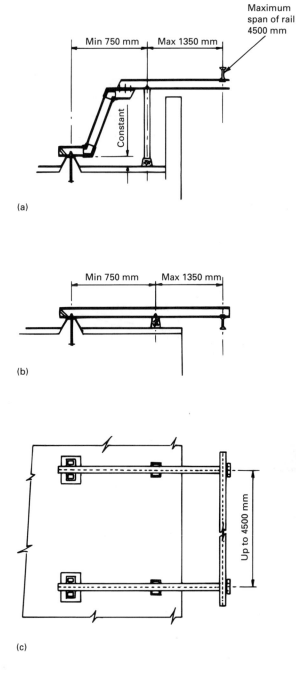

(a)

(b)

Figure 8.24 Cantilever support for a temporary access cradle: C = counterweight; T = tail length; W = weight of cradle, men and material; O = overhang. To balance, $C \times T = W \times O$. For safety $C \times T$ should not be less than three times $W \times O$

(c)

Figure 8.25 Fixed davits for the suspension of temporary cradles: (a) flat roof with parapet; (b) flat roof; (c) typical plan view

The **powered trolley and cradle** system represents the largest initial cost outlay for any of the systems examined so far, but this is also the quickest method of coverage for access to the face of the structure. Horizontal movements can be generated by the operative from the cradle by pressing the appropriate button to move the trolley on its roof-level trackway. Another button will allow vertical movements. The expense of this system will need to be considered against the very low attendant time that is needed when this system is provided (Figure 8.27).

British Standard 6037 outlines a guide to the safe use of permanent access equipment of this type [18].

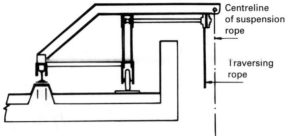

(a)

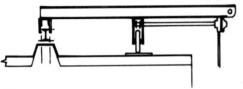

(b)

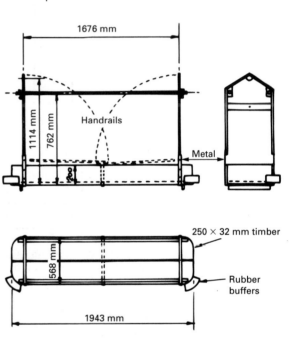

(c)

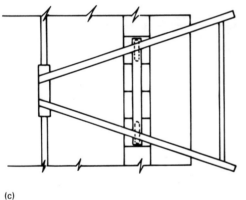

(d)

Figure 8.26 Moving trolley suspensions for temporary cradles (a) flat roof with parapet; (b) flat roof; (c) typical plane view; (d) typical standard steel-framed timber cradle

SERVICES: COST CONSIDERATIONS

The intention of this section is to provoke thought about the cost implications of selecting alternative solutions in service installations. In today's pressured economic climate, choice is not usually made on the grounds of initial costs alone, but rather on total costs, which include the in use cost as well. Costs in use or life cycle costs for services installations could include:

- running costs;
- maintenance costs;
- replacement costs.

Running costs relate, for example, to the consumption of fuel, and this in itself may have a considerable influence in the selection process. This may be simply illustrated by reference to the implications of heating fuels for domestic property (Table 8.1). This summary does of course make assumptions

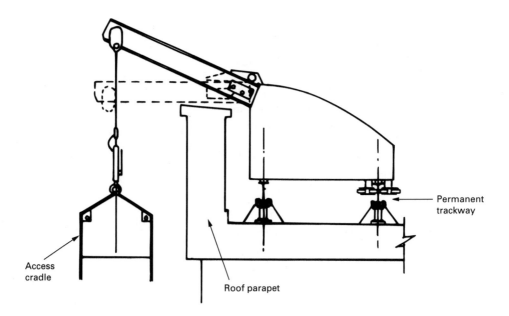

Figure 8.27 A powered cradle suspended from a powered trolley

about relative costs, but it serves to illustrate the point.

The seesaw analogy is also useful when contemplating decisions of this sort (Figure 8.28). A similar representation of initial costs against maintenance costs may also be made.

To allow the comparison of future costs, reference can be made to the use of **compound interest tables**. These tables fall basically under six major headings, and provide lists of multiplication factors:

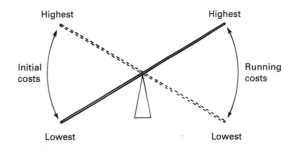

Figure 8.28 The balance between initial costs and running costs

- *Amt of 1 = amount of £1 table*: the multiplication factor to be applied when finding the sum to which £1 invested now will accumulate to in x years at y per cent interest;
- *PV of 1 = present value of £1 table*: the multiplication factor to be applied to find the sum that should be invested now to accumulate to £1 in x years at y per cent interest;
- *Amt of 1 pa = amount £1 per annum table*: the multiplication factor to be applied to find the sum to which £1 invested each year for x years

Table 8.1 *Costs of fuel for heating domestic property*

	Installation costs	Running costs
Electricity	Least expensive	Most expensive
Solid fuel	Second most expensive	Second most expensive
Gas	Most expensive	Least expensive

will accumulate to at y per cent interest;

- *PV of 1 pa = present value of £1 per annum table or years' purchase*: the multiplication factor to be applied when valuing the right to receive an income of £1 for x years at y per cent interest;
- *ASF = annual sinking fund table*; the multiplication factor to be applied to find the amount that should be invested annually for x years to accumulate to £1 at y per cent interest;
- *Annuity table*; the multiplication factor to be applied to assess the annual income receivable for x years following the investment of £1 at y per cent interest.

Of these tables, Amt of 1, PV of 1 and ASF may be of particular use when assessing long-term outlays to be made on alternative service installations.

For example, if inflation can be reasonably predicted the current cost of future expenditure may be assessed.

If a component of a heating system requires replacement after 15 years at a current cost of £800 and the borrowing rate is predicted at an average of 8 per cent over the next 15 years, then in 15 years' time the cost of the replacement will be:

		£800
$\times$ Amt of £1 for 15 years at 8 per cent	=	3.17217
Future outlay	=	£2537.74

If we know that in 20 years' time it will cost £1000 to replace a component of an air conditioning system and we can currently obtain 8 per cent interest on investments, we can assess how much should be invested now to accumulate to £1000 in 20 years:

		£1000
$\times$ PV of £1 for 20 years at 8 per cent	=	0.21454
Sum to be invested now	=	£214.54

If we would rather invest a sum annually to accumulate to the £1000 rather than place a lump sum now, the ASF table would indicate the annual saving needed:

		£1000
$\times$ ASF for 20 years at 8 per cent	=	0.021852
Sum to save annually	=	£21.85

To illustrate a simple comparison of three different air conditioning schemes, which have similar running costs but cost slightly different amounts to install and have differing needs in terms of the replacement of parts while in operation:

	Initial cost (£)	Replacement costs (£)
Scheme A	15 000	3 000 every 10 years
		15 000 after 20 years
Scheme B	14 000	10 000 after 15 years
		20 000 after 25 years
Scheme C	14 500	4 000 after 10 years
		20 000 after 20 years

Which of these schemes would cost least overall over a 35 year building life? On the face of it the answer to this question is scheme A, but evaluation of the long-term implications of the options at 8 per cent interest rate presents a much closer result than could be visualized initially:

Scheme A:

Initial cost		£15 000
Replacement of parts after 10 years	= £3 000	
× PV of £1 for 10 years at 8 per cent	= 0.46319	
		= £ 1 389.57
Replacement of parts after 20 years	= £15 000	
× PV of £1 for 20 years at 8 per cent	= 0.21454	
		= £ 3 218.10
Replacement of parts after 30 years	= £3 000	
× PV of £1 for 30 years at 8 per cent	= 0.09937	
		= £ 298.11
Total cost at today's date for A		= £ 19 905.78

Scheme B:

Initial cost		£14 000
Replacement of parts after 15 years	= £10 000	
× PV of £1 for 15 years at 8 per cent	= 0.31524	
		= £ 3 152.40
Replacement of parts after 25 years	= £20 000	
× PV of £1 for 25 years at 8 per cent	= 0.14601	
		= £ 2 920.20
Total cost at today's date for B		= £ 20 072.60

Scheme C:

Initial cost		£14 500
Replacement of parts after 10 years	= £4 000	
× PV of £1 for 10 years at 8 per cent	= 0.46319	
		= £ 1 852.76
Replacement of parts after 20 years	= £20 000	
× PV of £1 for 20 years at 8 per cent	= 0.21454	
		= £ 4 290.80
Total cost at today's date for C		= £ 20 643.56

Although in this analysis scheme A is the cheapest in overall cost terms, the adoption of A must be carefully considered. Scheme B has only a fractionally larger outlay than scheme A, but initially costs £1000 less to install than does scheme A.

The value of forecasting future outlays in this way when using the compound interest formulae may be useful, but it should be viewed in its true context, as it does contain weaknesses. The calculations generally presume that future conditions, rates of inflation and interest rates can all be predicted. The lives of buildings and components are also difficult to forecast. For more detailed information on the computation of the life cycle costs of building services components, as well as complete buildings, readers are referred to *Building Economics* [19]. Provided the calculations are viewed in the light of these limitations, then their use may prove worthy of adoption.

Other factors, such as inconvenience or loss of production during maintenance and replacement work, would be significant features when considering the adoption of alternatives. They also show that the application of these calculations may represent an oversimplification of the situation.

QUESTIONS

1 Outline the methods of structural accommodation available for service integration in a multi-storey office block.
2 Indicate the criteria that may be considered important when designing methods of service accommodation.
3 Suggest a form of suspended ceiling system suitable for rapid access to the concealed services.
4 Distinguish between shallow and deep cavity raised floors by providing a description of each form.
5 Comment on the layout and arrangement of services when conveyed within a structural method of accommodation such as a walkway duct.
6 In what ways may the design of a building be influenced when considering the available methods of vertical personnel movement?
7 Describe the safety features to be possessed by escalators.

8 Relate the 3 Ts and the flame triangle to the combustion processes that take place in a building fire.
9 What factors have to be considered in selecting a fire fighting system in the following buildings?
   (a) A multi-storey office block.
   (b) An underground car park.
   (c) A factory in which solvents are being used in an adhesive process.
   (d) An electric substation supplying a factory.
   (e) A large retail store
   (f) A cinema.
10 What classifications are given to the control of a fire?
11 Discuss the limitations of the 'first aid' methods used in fire-fighting.
12 Write a brief report to a client, informing him on the type of permanent fire-fighting systems he should install in the following areas of a new building:
   (a) an office block;
   (b) a manufacturing area in which a large amount of packing paper is stored;
   (c) a boardroom.
   State your reasons for the choice in each case.
13 What is the difference between a wet riser and a dry riser? State where each would be used.
14 Describe the operation of the three basic types of sprinkler system that are in common use.
15 By means of neat sketches show the structural requirements and builder's work necessary in a typical lift shaft.
16 What is the function of a counterweight in a lift installation?
17 Discuss the factors that have to be considered in selecting a lift for the following:
   (a) a hospital;
   (b) a loading bay in a warehouse;
   (c) an office block of 30 floors.
18 What are the advantages of an hydraulic lift over a electrical lift?
19 Various methods of call control may be used on lifts. Outline the advantages and disadvantages of each of these.
20 In what circumstances would you select an escalator in preference to a lift and why?
21 Compare the safety features of a lift and an

escalator. Include fire safety in your answer.

22 Outline the factors that are likely to influence the incidence of maintenance received by a building.

23 Describe the ratio that is a useful indicator of the efficiency of enclosure space given by different building shapes, and explain how it is calculated.

24 Explain the seesaw analogy as applied to expenditure on initial costs and running costs.

25 Outline the limitations and advantages of **two** forms of equipment that can allow access for maintenance of the exterior face of high-rise buildings.

REFERENCES

1 BS 5588 : Part 9 and BS 8313 : 1989 (replaces CP 413)

2 Building Regulations 1991, Part B, Approved Document B, clause B2/3/4, Appendix B, B4

3 BS 5655 : Part 1 : 1986 *Safety rules for the construction and installation of electric lifts*

4 BS 5655 : Part 6 : 1985 *Code of practice for the selection and installation of lifts.* See also CIBSE Guide B15 *Vertical transportation*

5 BS 5655 : Part 2 : 1988 *Specification for hydraulic lifts*

6 BS 5655 : Part 7 : 1982 *Specification for manual control devices, indicators and additional fittings*

7 BS 5656 : 1983 *Safety rules for the selection and installation of escalators*

8 Building Regulations 1991, Approved Document B, Clause B3

9 BS 5423 : 1987 *Specification for portable fire extinguishers*

10 BS 5423 : 1987 *Specification for portable fire extinguishers*

11 BS 6575 : 1985 *Specification for fire blankets*

12 BS 5306 : Part 1 : *Hydrant systems, hose reels and foam inlets*

13 BS 336 : 1980 *Specification for fire coupling and ancillary equipment*; BS 3169 : 1986 *Specification for first aid reel hoses for fire fighting purposes*; BS 3165 : 1986 *Rubber suction hoses for fire fighting purposes*; BS 5274 : 1985 *Specification for fire hose reels (water) for fixed installations*

14 BS 5041 : Parts 1–5 (various dates) Wet and dry risers. See also CIBSE Guide B5 *Fire safety engineering* (1986).

15 Building Regulations 1991, Approved Document B, B5.

16 BS 5588 : 1991 (10 parts) *Fire precautions in the design, construction and use of buildings*

17 BS 1139 : Part 3 *Specification for prefabricated access and working towers*

18 BS 6037 : *Code of practice for permanent installed access equipment*

19 I.H. Seeley, *Building Economics*, Macmillan (1996)

APPENDIX A. INTERPRETATION OF DRAWN INFORMATION

It is essential to understand the symbols shown on engineering services drawings, as these provide a speedy and standard method of reading the drawing.

The field of symbols is in a state of flux, as British Standards are being harmonized into the new CEN (European Committee for Standardization) standards, which cover the EU, and ISO (International Standards Organization) standards covering countries throughout the world. Before listing symbols on a drawing it is prudent to ensure that they meet the latest requirements of the above organizations.

The list below gives some indication of the wide range of publications that have to be consulted in order to obtain a symbol. By the year 2000, however, most of these will have merged into new CEN or ISO standards.

- BS 1553 : 1977 *General engineering Part 1. Piping systems and plant*
- BS 1635 : 1990 *Fire protection drawings*
- BS 6217 : 1989 *Graphical symbols for electrical systems*
- BS 3939 : Parts 1–13 (various dates) *Graphical symbols for electric power, telecommunications and electronic diagrams*
- ISO 4067-1 *Graphical symbols for plumbing, heating, ventilation and ducting*

- BS EN 60617 *Graphical symbols for diagrams*
- BS EN 61175 *Designations for signals and connections (electrical)*
- BS 6465 : 1984 *Sanitary installations*
- BS 8005 : Parts 0–5 *Sewage*
- BS 8010 : Various parts and sections of codes of practice for pipelines
- BS 6700 : 1987 *Specification for design installation, testing and maintenance of services supplying water for domestic use within buildings and their curtilage*
- BS 5572 : 1978 *Code of practice for sanitary pipework*

The abbreviation CENELEC may be seen; this relates to the European Electrical standards, which are replacing the British Standard specifications.

SYMBOLS ASSOCIATED WITH THE COMPONENTS OF BUILDING SERVICES INSTALLATIONS

The symbols below are produced with the permission of the British Standards Institution. Care has to be taken in using computer-aided design (CAD) packages, as the symbols used in these may not meet the requirements of international standards.

Pipes, ducts, drains and sewers
Symbols

Applications

——————————— Any type

Pipe, duct, drain
or sewer showing
direction of flow

▶ Direction of flow

Showing fall in direction
of flow

⊢→ Gradient in direction of flow

Fall 1:50

⋈ Straight two port

Showing rise in direction
of flow

Rise 1:50

▷ Angled two port

Symbols

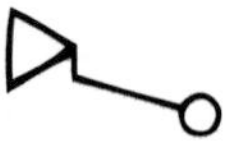

⋈ Three port

Ballcock

▷ Non-return (check)

Lockshield
straight

⋈ Pressure reducing

Lockshield
angled

Lockshield
oblique

Gas meter
GAS

Water meter
WATER

Manholes and gullies

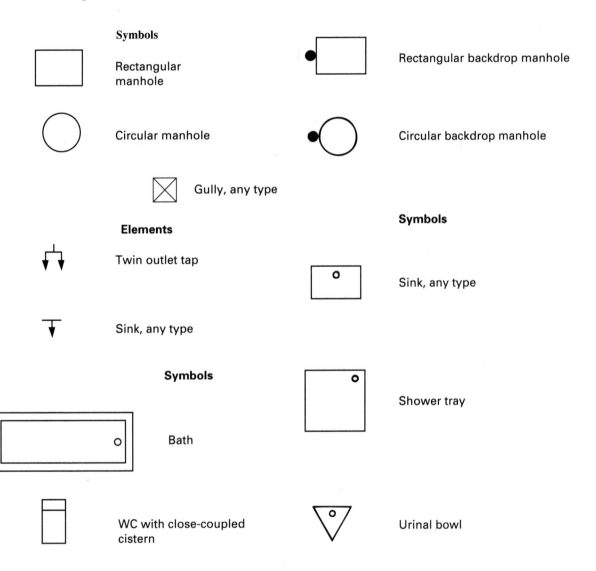

Symbols

Rectangular manhole

Rectangular backdrop manhole

Circular manhole

Circular backdrop manhole

Gully, any type

Elements

Twin outlet tap

Symbols

Sink, any type

Sink, any type

Symbols

Shower tray

Bath

WC with close-coupled cistern

Urinal bowl

Pipework components

Symbols

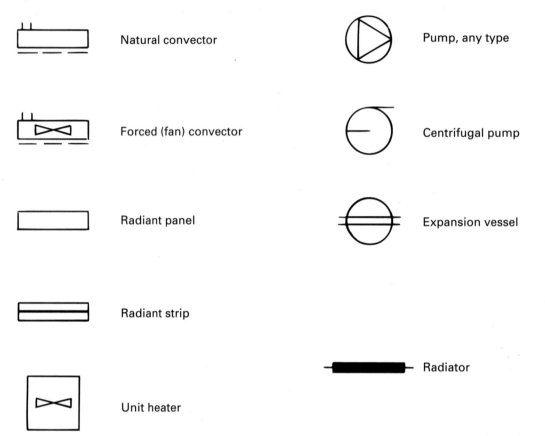

Natural convector	Pump, any type
Forced (fan) convector	Centrifugal pump
Radiant panel	Expansion vessel
Radiant strip	
	Radiator
Unit heater	

Air-handling equipment

Symbols

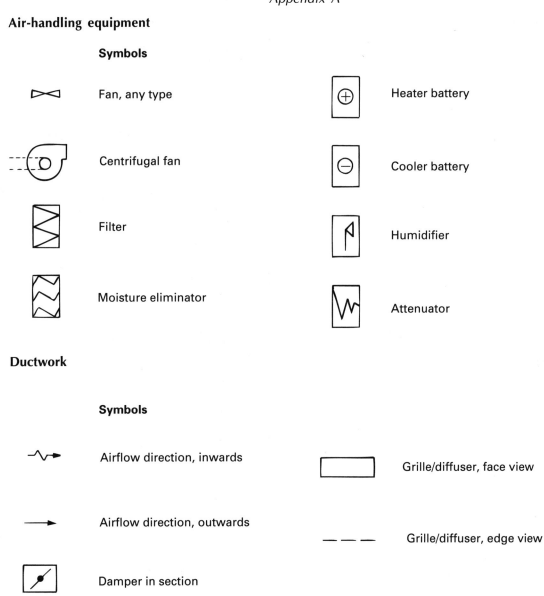

Fan, any type

Heater battery

Centrifugal fan

Cooler battery

Filter

Humidifier

Moisture eliminator

Attenuator

Ductwork

Symbols

Airflow direction, inwards

Grille/diffuser, face view

Airflow direction, outwards

Grille/diffuser, edge view

Damper in section

Electrical services

Switches

Power outlets

Elements

Symbols

 One-pole switching device

 Socket outlet to BS 1363, any type

 Two-pole switching device

Socket outlet to BS 1363 with indicating lamp

 Three-pole switching device

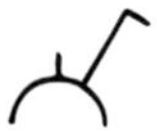

Socket outlet to BS 1363 with one-pole switch

Four-pole switching device

2
Socket outlet to BS 1363, two gang

Pull cord operation

Symbols

 One-pole, one-way

 One-pole, two-way

Electrical services
Supply and distribution

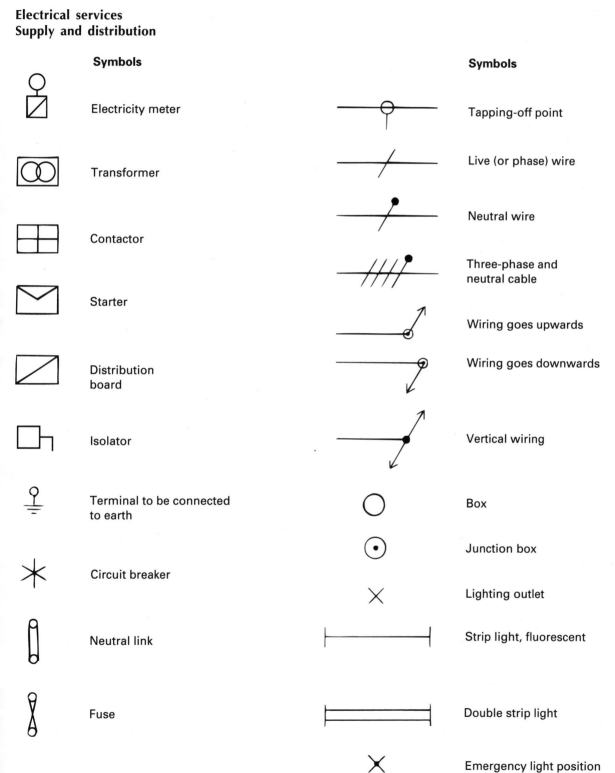

Symbols		Symbols	
	Electricity meter		Tapping-off point
	Transformer		Live (or phase) wire
	Contactor		Neutral wire
	Starter		Three-phase and neutral cable
	Distribution board		Wiring goes upwards
	Isolator		Wiring goes downwards
	Terminal to be connected to earth		Vertical wiring
	Circuit breaker		Box
	Neutral link		Junction box
	Fuse		Lighting outlet
			Strip light, fluorescent
			Double strip light
			Emergency light position

APPENDIX B. UNITS AND EQUATIONS

In any study of building services engineering it is essential to have an understanding of the units and equations used, as these provide an appreciation of the plant operation.

Rather than just giving a shopping list of the units, some of the basic equations encountered have been given, stating their application and the nature of the units involved.

EQUATIONS USED IN HEAT AND MASS FLOW

A very important equation is that used in the determination of the sensible heat flow that takes place in a fluid, which may be either liquid or air.

$$\frac{\text{Sensible heat}}{\text{flow}} = \frac{\text{Mass flow in}}{\text{unit time}} \times \frac{\text{Specific heat}}{\text{capacity}} \times \frac{\text{Temperature}}{\text{difference}}$$

Inserting the units used in this equation:

kW (or kJ/s) = kg/s × kJ/kg °C × °C

Expressing in symbol form:

$$Q = m \times C_p \times \Delta t \tag{1}$$

An everyday application of Equation (1) is the determination of the water flow rate required for the sizing of a heat emitter.

In calculating the annual energy consumption for heating systems, the use of the kilowatt (10^3 W) results in a rather cumbersome large number, and it is normal to use the megawatt, MW (10^6 W) or gigawatt, GW (10^9 W).

Once the rate of heat loss from a room is known, a radiator or other type of heat emitter has to be selected. The pipe that supplies water to this radiator must be capable of providing the correct mass flow rate (kg/s) for a given temperature difference. The temperature difference for a low-temperature hot water system is normally taken as being 10 °C (80 °C flow and 70 °C return), the specific heat

capacity, C_p, of water is taken as 4.18 kJ/kg °C. Note that the value of C_p varies with temperature and pressure.

If the mass flow rate is too low, the radiator will give out less heat than required, resulting in inadequate room air temperature during winter conditions.

A simple example will illustrate the use of this equation.

Example

A radiator catalogue states that a given-sized radiator will emit 3.0 kW. Determine the mass flow rate of water that is required to the radiator if the flow temperature is 80 °C and the return temperature is 70 °C.

Solution

Use Equation (1) : $Q = m \times C_p \times \Delta t$

Transposing in order to determine the mass flow rate (kg/s):

$$m = \frac{Q}{C_p \times \Delta t}$$

where Q = heat output required from radiator (3 kW); Δt = temperature difference between the flow and return (10 °C); at the mean water temperature in the radiator (75 °C), the specific heat capacity C_p is 4.194 kJ/kg °C.

Hence the mass flow rate required at these conditions is:

$$m = \frac{30}{4.194 \times 10.0}$$

$$= 0.07153 \text{ kg/s}$$

Should the heating application require a warm air system to be used, the value of C_p for dry air would be taken as being approximately 1.01 kJ/kg °C. The temperature difference in this case would normally be slightly higher than 10 °C.

HEAT LOSS

The rate of heat loss from a space can be expressed simply as:

$$Q_p = (Q_f + Q_v) \Delta t \qquad (2)$$

where Q_p = the heat output of the boiler plant (kW); Q_f = the rate of heat loss through the elements of the building fabric (kW); and

$$Q_f = \Sigma (A \times U) \Delta t$$

where Σ = the summation of; A = the area of the elements considered (m²), i.e. wall, glass, etc.; U = the thermal transmission coefficient (W/m² °C) (the values of U must meet the requirements of the Building Regulations).

Q_v = the rate of heat loss by ventilation (kW) = (0.33 NV) Δt; Δt = the difference in temperature between the inside design temperature (t_{ai}) and the outside design temperature (t_{ao}); N = the number of air changes that take place per hour (for natural ventilation see CIBSE Guide A4, while for mechanical ventilation see CIBSE Guide B2); V = volume of the space being considered (m³). The constant 0.33 is determined from:

$$\frac{\text{Specific heat capacity, } C_p \times \text{Air density, } \rho}{\text{Seconds in one hour}}$$

That is:

$$\frac{1010 \text{ J/kg °C} \times 1.2 \text{ kg/m}^3}{3600} \approx 0.33 \qquad (3)$$

The answers obtained for the value of Q_p are only approximate, as the mode of heating must be considered, (radiators or convectors). The method of heating used requires correction factors F_1 and F_2 to be applied to the values of Q_f and Q_v. These correction factors are obtained from the *CIBSE Guide A9* Table A 9.1–A 9.7.

In many instances, the U value has to be calculated from:

$$U = \frac{1}{\Sigma R} \qquad (4)$$

where ΣR is the summation of the various structural thermal resistances (m² °C/W). The value of R is determined by dividing the thickness (m) of the material by its thermal conductivity λ (W/m °C). The values of thermal conductivity and surface resistance are obtained from the CIBSE Guide A3.

The following equation is used to determine the U value for a composite structure:

$$U = \frac{1}{R_{si} + \dfrac{l_1}{\lambda_1} + \dfrac{l_2}{\lambda_2} + R_a + \dfrac{l_3}{\lambda_3} + R_{so}} \qquad (5)$$

where R_{si} = inside surface resistance (m² °C/W); R_a = resistance of air gap (m² °C/W); R_{so} = outside surface resistance (m² °C/W); l = thickness of material (m); λ = thermal conductivity of material (W/m °C); and suffices 1, 2, etc. relate to the material.

The above equation can be extended to include any number of l/λ. Note: this is the same as R.

To determine the surface temperature:

$$Q_f = U \times A \times \Delta t$$

or

$$Q_f = \frac{\Delta t}{\Sigma R}$$

or $\Delta t = \Sigma R \times Q_f$

The inside surface temperature is determined from:

$$t_{si} = t_{ai} - (R_{si} \times Q_f) \qquad (6)$$

While the external surface temperature is determined from:

$$t_{so} = t_{ao} + (R_{so} \times Q_f) \qquad (7)$$

where R_{si} = inside surface resistance (m² °C/W); R_{so} = outside surface resistance (m² °C/W).

THE CONTINUITY EQUATION

Use is made of this equation in order to determine any one of three variables when the other two are known.

The variables considered may relate to the flow of air, or water, and are:

Q = quantity of flow, m³/s for air and kg/s for water;

A = the cross-sectional area of the pipe or duct (m²);

V = the velocity of fluid in the duct or pipe (m/s)

The equation is

$$Q = A \times V \tag{8}$$

A typical application of this equation is that of duct sizing.

Example

A run of ductwork in an air-conditioning system has to carry 2 m³/s of air at a velocity of 10 m/s. What is the required cross-sectional area of the duct?

Answer

We apply $Q = A \times V$, where $Q = 2$ m³/s, $A = ?$, $V = 10$ m/s.
  Transposing:

$$A = \frac{Q}{V}$$

Therefore

$$A = \frac{2.0}{10} = 0.2\text{m}^2$$

Hence a duct having a cross-sectional area of 0.2 m² is required; this may be either circular or rectangular.

ELECTRICAL

When electrical heating is used it is necessary to determine the rating of an element, in order that the required kW output is provided.

Example

A 3.0 kW immersion heater is fitted in a water tank of 0.2 m³ (200 litre). Determine the time taken to heat the water from 10 °C to 80 °C:

(a) assuming the process is 100 per cent efficient. (no heat loss);

(b) assuming the efficiency is 90 per cent (10 per cent of the heat input is lost by poor quality thermal insulation).

Answer

The basic equation is $Q = m \times C_p \times \Delta t$, where $Q = 3.0$ kW; 1 m³ of water weighs 1000 kg or 1 tonne and therefore 0.2 m³ = 200 kg; Δt = temperature difference = (80 − 10) = 70 °C.

(a) The electrical input is 3.0 kW $\times$ time in hours $= 3 \times t$. As 1 kWh $= 3.6 \times 10^6$ J, heat output:

$$Q = \text{kg} \times \Delta t \times C_p$$

Taking C_p as 4190 J/kg °C:

$$Q = \frac{200 \times 70 \times 4190}{3.6 \times 106}$$

$$= \textbf{16.29 kWh}$$

Hence $3\,t = 16.29$

and $t = \dfrac{16.29}{3.0} = \textbf{5.43 hours} = \textbf{5 hours 25.8 minutes}$

(b) In this case the heating process is only 90 per cent efficient, so the heating process will take longer than that in case (a):

$$t = 5.43 \text{ hours} \times \frac{100}{90}$$

= 6.03 hours = 6 hours 1.8 minutes

As case (b) takes longer to heat up, the electrical usage will be greater than that in case (a): hence the running costs will be greater, showing the need for thermal insulation.

COMBUSTION

Combustion calculations allow the determination of the quantity of fuel necessary to provide sufficient heat to meet a building's heat losses.

In order to carry out this calculation, the calorific value of the fuel is required; this is the heat contained in a unit weight or volume of fuel. For a solid fuel the units of calorific value are kJ/kg; for a liquid fuel they are MJ/litre, and for a gaseous fuel they are MJ/m^3.

In theory, all the heat contained in the fuel can be used. If the fuel contains moisture or hydrogen, steam is produced, which on leaving through the chimney will take with it heat that is not used for the building's heating system.

The theoretical heat content in the fuel is known as the gross calorific value: hence the moisture liberated up the stack is reducing the useful heat contained in the fuel. In making allowances for this, the net calorific value is used. This is obtained by deducting the latent heat in the vapour content of the combustion products, when cooled, from the gross calorific value.

Typical calorific values are listed in Table B1. The use of these values is best shown by means of an example.

Table B.1 *Typical calorific values*

Fuel	Gross CV (MJ/kg)	Net CV (MJ/kg)
Coal	30.60	29.65
Gas oil	45.60	42.80
Natural gas	53.42	48.16

Example

A building has a design heat loss of 600 kW. Determine how many of kg of solid, liquid or gaseous fuels are required if the combustion efficiency of each burner is 80 per cent. For simplicity, all the calorific values have been given as MJ/kg.

Answer

If the combustion process is 100 per cent efficient, the fuel required is simply:

$$\text{kg of fuel required} = \frac{\text{Heat requirement in kW}}{\text{Net heat content in fuel kJ/kg}} \quad (9)$$

For coal

$$= \frac{600 \text{ kW}}{29650 \text{ kJ/kg}} = 0.0202 \text{ kg/s}$$

Note that the MJ/kg must be converted to kJ/kg for consistency with the kW. As the combustion process is only 80 per cent efficient, the fuel required will have to be greater than this calculated amount by:

$$0.0202 \times \frac{100}{80}$$

= 0.0252 kg/s of coal

The calculations for gas oil results in a requirement of 0.0175 kg/s, while natural gas is 0.01557 kg/s.

Considering the units used above:

$$1 \text{ J} = 1 \text{ W/s}$$

Hence:

$$\frac{\text{Heat load kW (kJ/s)}}{\text{kJ/kg}}$$

which on cancelling out gives kg/s.

INDEX